A Matrix for Community Music Therapy Practice

Stuart Wood

Barcelona
PUBLISHERS

A Matrix for Community Music Therapy Practice

Copyright © 2016 by Barcelona Publishers

Print ISBN: 9781937440817
E-ISBN: 9781937440824

Distributed throughout the world by:
Barcelona Publishers
10231 Plano Rd.
Dallas TX 75238
Website: www.barcelonapublishers.com
SAN 298-6299

Cover design: © 2015 Frank McShane

This book is dedicated to all of my teachers

Acknowledgements

My heartfelt thanks go to Kenneth Bruscia for the opportunity to write this book. I am deeply grateful for his eagle eye and kind critique. Eternal thanks also to Gary Ansdell and Mercédès Pavlicevic, who guided me through most (if not all) of the thinking that has gone into this text. This is a pantheon to die for.

I have written here about things done under the equally divine supervision of Rachel Verney, and management of Jim Marr and Scott Glickman. They, along with the support of Barbara Hughes and my music therapy team across the UK and Ireland, have have made this book possible.

In the academic journey contained here, colleagues Satomi Kondo, Harumi Suzuki, Barbara Hesser, Alan Turry, Ken Aigen, Brynjulf Stige, Neta Spiro, Evangeline Cheng, and Brian Abrams have signposted, accommodated, and fed my enquiry. My doctoral friends Claire Flower, Giorgos Tsiris, and Kjetel Hjørnevik have challenged and consoled in equal measure. The companionship of Valarie Wilson and P. A. Skantze continues to inspire me, musically and creatively. And for the daybreak coffees and human genius, I thank Jack Tan. No better resonating chamber exists anywhere.

I acknowledge finally the presence and faith of the people whose stories I relay here. They have always had something to teach me, and I think they may yet have something for you, too.

Contents

Acknowledgements iv

List of Figures x

Preface xi
    A Question xi
    Grounding Themes xi
    A Practical Discipline xi
    A Creative Profession xii
    A Complex Discourse xii
    A Simple Idea xiv
    Overview of Chapters xiv
    Personal Declaration xv
    Purpose of Book xvi

Introduction 3
    Key Themes 3
    What Is Community Music Therapy? 4
    Ecological Perspective 5
    Key Signatures 5
    Music 6
    Need 6
    The Person 7
    Matrix Thinking 7
    Formats 7
    Aims 8
    Context 9
    Evaluation 9
    Theory 9
    Creating a Matrix 10

The Music Matrix 13
    "Everything is Music" 13
    "FACETs" of Music 16
    Range of Musical Impact 17
    Order, Type, and Reach of Impact 17
    "Order" 18

"Type" 18
"Reach" 18
Musical Formats 19
Music Is Multimodal 19
Application in Music Therapy 22
Multiplicity 23

Recognizing CoMT **27**
Formulation of CoMT 27
The Ecological Perspective 27
Theoretical Framework 28
Critiques of CoMT 32
Formulation of "Music" 34
Music as Milieu 35
Formulation of "Need" 36
Assessment and Evaluation 36
According to Individual Symptomatic Need 37
According to Wider Ecological Considerations 38
Formulation of "The Person" 40
Individualist Perspectives 40
Ecological Perspectives 42
Summary 43
Toward Formats 44

Matrix of Formats **47**
Scrap Metal Project 47
From Therapy to Community 47
What Is Progress? 48
PJ's Progress 50
Individuals, Groups, Communities 52
Facilitating a Project 53
The Scrap Metal Concert 55
Formats and Activities 56
Matrix Diagram of Formats 57
Implications for Theory 58
Emergence 58
Toward Aims 62

Matrix of Aims **65**

Five Seasons 65
Early Individual Work 65
Whose Aim Is It? 66
New Aims 69
Projects Emerge from Practice 71
New Context, New Evaluation 72
One Size Fits All? 74
Practical Activities of Evaluation 75
Diverse Activities 75
Link Between Evaluation and Planning 75
Problem of Communicating 77
Focus of Evaluation 79
Aims and Timing 79
Conceptual Tools 80
Diverse Conceptual Tools 80
Source of Conceptual Tools 80
Multiple Time Frames 81
Planning and Goals 81
Witnessed Practice 82
Professional Identity 82
Professional Duty 83
Professional Expectations 84
The Workplace Shapes Practice 84
Responding to Context 84
Collaborative Practice 85
Increased Number of Participants 85
Reflexivity Is Complex 85
Intimations of Multiplicity 86
Capturing Multiplicity: Functional Interaction 86
Dimensions 87
Politics of Aims 88
Matrix Flowchart of Aims 89
Matrix Thinking About Aims 89
Implications for Theory 92
What Is a Rhizome? 94
Seeing Music as a Rhizome 95
Toward Context 96

Matrix of Context **97**

"Pam" in Context 97
The Context of Care Homes 97
"JUNK" 99
The Starting Point 99
The Context of a Body 99
The Context of a Project 100
Creating a New Context 101
The Context of (a) Company 102
Music and Organizations 103
Discourses of Health Care 103
Direct Contact with Music 104
Discourse 1: Personal Biographical 104
Discourse 2: Professional Music Therapy 105
Discourse 3: Dementia Care 109
Discourse 4: Design/Layout 109
Discourse 5: Sales 110
Sharing Across the Organization 111
Discourse 5: Sales 111
Discourse 6: Display 111
Discourse 7: Cinema 112
Discourse 8: Music Specialism 112
Discourse 9: Nursing 114
Discourse 10: Training and Development 115
Discourse 11: Management 116
Discourse 12: Health Care Culture 116
Discourse 13: Health Care Business Practice 117
Public Dissemination and Broadcast 118
Discourse 14: PR 118
Discourse 15: Mass Media 119
Discourse 16: Research 119
Discourse 17: Fund-raising 121
The Range of Context 121
Matrix of Context 123
Implications for Theory 124
Performativity 124
Toward Evaluation 127

Matrix of Evaluation **127**
"Paddy" 127

Getting to Know Paddy 127
Toward New Knowledge 131
Multiple Values 133
"Evaluation" in Music Therapy 134
Character and Scope of Evaluation 134
Assessment and Evaluation 134
Evaluating Art? 135
Methods of Evaluation 136
Purpose and Authorship 136
Tracking Wider Impact 138
Objectivity and Validity 139
Strategic Uses of Evaluation 140
Diagnosis 140
Funding and Professional Status 141
Music Therapy Evaluation Is Performative 142
Matrix Diagram of Evaluation 143
Functional Interaction Matrix Assessment (*fi*-ma) 143
Assessment Methodology 144
Assessment Method 145
"Function" and "Interaction" 145
Dimensions 146
Subskills 147
Where Is Music? 148
Implications for Theory 148
Simultaneity 148
Performing Person, Performing Music 150
Politics of Evaluation Language 151
Procedure and Content 152
Collaborative Strategies 153
Inclusion and Ethics 153
Considerations for "Effective" Evaluation Strategies 154
Toward "FACETs" 155

Conclusion **157**
Summary 157
FACETs of CoMT 157
Formats 157
Aims 158
Context 158

Evaluation 158
Theory 159
Emergence 159
Performativity 159
Implications 160
The Essential-Contingent 160
The Single-Multiple 161
The Material-Semiotic 162
The Intrinsic-Instrumental 163
The Clinical-Communal 164
An Answer 165

Reference List **167**

Index **191**

List of Figures

Fig. 1: The three-stage work plan 48
Fig. 2: The matrix of musical formats 58
Fig. 3: Five insights on evaluation 74
Fig. 4: Matrix of aims 91
Fig. 5: Extract of microanalysis 113
Fig. 6: Matrix of discourses 123
Fig. 7: Music therapy subskills 147/8
Fig. 8: Assessment grid 149

Preface

A Question:

"What can this gentleman *do*, Stuart?"

The consultant-in-rehabilitation wanted answers. It was a multidisciplinary team meeting, in the early days of a new post. I had already heard the psychologist, physiotherapist, lead nurse, occupational therapist, health care assistant, and administrator review their week's work on the neurological ward. It was my turn to say how my practice (at that time, a relatively new subdivision of music therapy becoming known more widely as Community Music Therapy) would help. In particular, the consultant wanted to know first what his patient could do, and second, what would I now do with him ...

Here was double trouble. First, I had about five seconds to communicate how music helps neurological patients, explaining the many facets of musical experience to people with diverse professional discourses and values. On top of that, and like many music therapists, I didn't yet know what I was going to do. I had a broad outline of my project scope and my work locations, but apart from that, there was little I could predict. Back then in 2001, the idea of engaging with patients in flexible ways that were suited to their changing context was of course part of many music therapists' approach, but not widely reported. The professional language for it certainly wasn't tripping off my tongue. I am grateful that in this book I have the opportunity to say now what I wish I could have said then.

Grounding Themes

A Practical Discipline

Perhaps my first problem in that multidisciplinary team meeting was that in Community Music Therapy (from now on I will use the abbreviation CoMT), like many other traditions of and approaches to music therapy, we discover what it is that we do by doing it. Our discipline is not just contained in practice, it is revealed by it. This is why so much of music therapy is reflective, retrospective, and, indeed, recorded. So whilst we have our professional checks and balances (such as codes of practice, reflective work, post-session notes, video and audio analysis), we also have a musician's trust in the unfolding of creativity: in what we can't yet know and will only later describe. My approach to CoMT is that it is particularly practice-led and yet requires a facility with theory in order to be effective.

A Creative Profession

The second impediment to giving a snappy answer was that whilst CoMT is revealed in practice, this practice is also pretty diverse. Both the processes of artistic production and of wellness are based on cycles of growth and diversity. To trust in music therapy practice therefore means that we trust in change, in creative leaps, and in modes of knowing and nonknowing. This is particularly relevant to those within CoMT who foreground collaboration, co-creativity, and social capital within their work. CoMT is the emergent product of a profession that knows about things that do not stay the same, about how things grow, and about the bold risks that creativity can demand of us.

A Complex Discourse

The third consideration, had I had the presence of mind at the time to realise it, was that music manifested very differently according to the world views and interests of each person in that meeting. The academic discipline of music therapy itself has matured into a vast range of voices, concerns, and perspectives. Recent music therapy publications (Aigen, 2014; Ansdell, 2014a) have demonstrated that our practice and creativity generate quite an array of interdisciplinary perspectives. This alone does not make the discourse of CoMT complex. Instead, what makes CoMT complex is that it explicitly aims to characterize and enhance what happens when those perspectives interrelate.

CoMT operates within a discourse that describes effects that are created out of the interactions of physical, emotional, psychological, social, and cultural activity. My own perspective is that this is its prime contribution to our profession. Other branches of music therapy and of related disciplines can already describe and account well for those subblocks (such as neuromusicology, music psychology, and theories of communicative musicality). The usefulness of CoMT is in how it can provide ways of talking at an emergent level, that is, how it can come to account for phenomena that cannot be subdivided into their constituent parts without losing something.

An early example of this from the canon of CoMT literature is the Ripple Effect (Pavlicevic & Ansdell, 2004, p. 16). This uncomplicated idea is in fact a classic complex device, in that it points to the very musical phenomenon of unpredictable change. The Ripple Effect works both within a person and amongst numbers of people, through a process of resonance. It also operates in structures beyond individuals, such as organizations, institutions, or cultures. That resonance is physical but also a metaphor for social and cultural reproduction. We understand ripples in series, a singular disturbance that comes from and points to another. A ripple is more than one thing, yet still singular. It is understood in terms that have to relate to its previous, or next, occurrence: timing, distance, relative size, trigger, and impact. A ripple is a disturbance repeated, and, much like a pulse, it requires at least two repetitions to become one. Also, ripples move and create movement. Complexity describes things in motion and is used to describe the change that follows.

Another device that has come to be associated with CoMT is the matrix (Wood, 2006). A matrix is a formation that organizes elements within a system, usually providing a nonhierarchical structure, such as a grid or a web, to model how those elements interrelate. The etymology of the word relates to materials within which other elements are contained and grow, such as rock matrices that hold gems, printing matrices that hold letter blocks to form words, and, of course, the womb.

I view music as a dynamic form of matrix for individual and social organization. It is therefore apt to describe how we might approach the use of music within music therapy. Originally, I adopted the term to illustrate how we might approach the formats of music-making within a music therapy service. I suggested that in most music therapy traditions there was a professional tendency to favour individual, dyadic encounters as the best format in which to do music therapy. I offered that in CoMT there need be no such tendency, and, instead, that there should be an equal approach to all modes of music-making, chosen and adapted to suit and protect the different participants encountered in the work. The matrix will be used throughout this book, modelling a range of aspects of CoMT.

A Simple Idea

The complex technology with which I would expect all readers to be familiar is of course music itself. With its attendant codes of notation, its terminology, its many modes of practice, and its way of operating, the discourse of music is our best language for its own complexity. This may explain why much of the literature on CoMT currently seems to arise out of music-centred approaches or otherwise to read as being commensurate with it. Increasingly, however, the central ideas of collaboration, being practice-led, and music's simultaneous impact on personal and political levels, resonate beyond the music-centred literature into such fields as feminist or resource-oriented music therapy, too.

This book will not be an apologetics for a new kind of music therapy. It describes a way of doing music therapy with which many might identify, even if they do not use the term "CoMT". In line with the founding authors from the canon of CoMT (Stige & Aarø, 2012, for example), I hope to build on established ways of recognizing and understanding aspects of practice, rather than make the case for a new model. The simple idea at the start of this book is this: When we acknowledge how music manifests in individuals and the many groupings they form, when we trust the process of artistic production and human wellness, and when we account for this professionally, we are most probably doing CoMT. I hope that the rest of this text will provide useful ways of getting to know it better.

Overview of Chapters

This book's overall aim is to draw together the main themes associated with CoMT. In Chapter One, I will set these themes out in more detail and provide an entry point to the main theory elements. Chapter Two explores how I think about music "itself" as a matrix. In Chapter Three, I will discuss how CoMT is formulated in music therapy literature, setting out the key features by which CoMT can be recognized.

The rest of the book will be built around what are for me significant facets of CoMT practice. Taking the word "FACET" as an acronym, I will explore five aspects: Formats, Aims, Context, Evaluation, and Theory. Four chapters describe practical CoMT with four extraordinary people. You will meet PJ, who went on a musical odyssey from hospital to scrap yard, improvising music with every step; Caryl, whose compositions were performed by a local choir; Pam, who galvanized a whole care home company around her musical narratives; and Paddy, whose musicality showed everyone around him what he could really do. Each of those accounts will help explore a different facet and offer a matrix structure for navigating it. The fifth aspect, Theory, is present in the book, but as a pervasive element, woven in to each chapter as a reflection on the theme. The matrix of Theory is in the thinking that emerges in relation to practice. Eyebrows may raise when you encounter sections on slime-mold, rhizomes, and the fractal-faceted eyes of flies. Bear with me. In trying to find ways of describing the natural operation of music amongst us, I have found myself turning to theories that illustrate concepts with examples from nature itself. I am in good company, as you will see.

I have tried to keep everything as close to practice as I can. This is where I position myself, but also I feel it is where CoMT speaks best, too. All the same, I have included thoughts from two research studies as examples. In Chapters Five and Six, you will find discussions of aims and context illustrated by my doctoral studies from 2014. These are included because they are practical examples of how the themes are experienced in daily life. I also include, in Chapter Seven, a proposal for the starting point toward CoMT evaluation. This is offered as a trigger to further discussion and will hopefully lead to new discoveries. The text concludes with a review of the book's main points; a summary of the themes contained within the facets of CoMT; and an observation of how these factors can both inform new practice and lend support to the ongoing development of music therapy as a whole.

Personal Declaration

I trained as a music therapist at the Nordoff Robbins London Centre, 1998–2000. My early practice spanned a community mental health drop-in centre, a community college, a school, a neurological rehabilitation unit, and a care home. My curiosity has always been driven by the complex relationships between the values and practices inherent in these diverse settings. As a researcher, I have found systems-based theories (such as aesthetic and psychosocial accounts of music therapy, neuromusicology, and music sociology) to be most relevant to this set of interests. The thoughts contained in this book are inspired by my teachers, whether my encounters have been directly as a student, colleague, and therapist or remotely through reading their work.

Purpose of Book

Many of us have perhaps had a moment like the question dropped on me by the consultant-in-rehabilitation, followed also by the post-hoc recrimination about what we "should have said". In one respect, this book is intended to set out in long form an answer to the question of how music therapy can help when used in a flexible program and what it shows us about people when we let it manifest in diverse formats. To put it another way, it aims to explore how music therapy enables music to be present, helpfully—both uniquely in the inner world of one person and yet simultaneously amongst different configurations of people, whether those configurations are social, institutional, or cultural. In writing, I have been inspired by the lively and "thought-aloud" style of ethnographers such as Latour, Law, and Mol.

This book will present my perspective on practices and processes associated with CoMT. It will consider how those practices and processes interrelate and what is produced when they are put into action. In order to frame what emerges out of that action, relevant aspects of theory will be woven into each chapter. This is not a compendium of CoMT practice or theory. We have excellent resources, in the shape of, amongst others, Ansdell (2002), Stige (2002), Pavlicevic and Ansdell (2004), Stige et al. (2010), Stige and Aarø (2012), and Ansdell (2014a). Instead, here you have a personal point of view, responding to and riffing off that foundation. Like all the music therapy literature that I value, it is motivated primarily by the question, *"How can I help?"*, so if that's your question, too, welcome along.

A MATRIX FOR COMMUNITY MUSIC THERAPY PRACTICE

Chapter I

INTRODUCTION

Key Themes

On the surface, this book is about CoMT. Scratch that surface and you will find that it rather quickly points to a more universal observation about music and wellness. That observation is that music and wellness can be seen as the same thing. Slightly further in, it seems to say that not only are music and wellness somehow the same thing, but also that everything can also be understood as music. The way we create knowledge about our brains, minds, relationships, practices, and social lives is musical. In CoMT, everything we do in or around music is potentially useful in the service of wellness. In some ways, this book is about how we can think about the use of everything. No grand designs there, then.

The more modest ambition here is to discuss facets of CoMT primarily from a practical point of view. CoMT theory doesn't make that easy, because it explicitly avoids (for the most part) definitions and prescriptions of practice. CoMT comes from a belief that music is a manifestation of wellness happening, whether that is within a person's immune system, or across a crowd singing at the World Series, or anywhere in between. For that reason, CoMT sees its work as eliciting and harnessing the healthy organization of real life understood musically, rather than applying sounds to illness, as if those sounds were a pill or a treatment. It is not the only music therapy approach that works that way, but it is unique in its way of thinking about it.

To begin to think about some of the processes involved in CoMT, we need new concepts. First, we have to accept that CoMT resists definition. You won't find a definition of CoMT in most literature, and you will not find one here, except if you look between the lines. You will, however, find a serious consideration of how this type of practice is recognized and put together so that it is robust and accountable. Second, we need to understand music as the manifestation of diverse things being organized, rather than as a specialist art form that has healing powers. That sort of terminology is useful rhetoric but grossly limiting with regard to what music can really do. To think about music in this alternative way, we draw on concepts of emergence, the rhizome, and the matrix. We look at the way life manifests musically, rather than how (some "expert") people conjure up sounds in situations that are framed as clinical. We also have to look seriously at how our professional concerns manifest and operate within this alternative approach to music therapy. Our main areas of attention here are in the "FACETs" that I associate with CoMT practice: the formats, aims, context, evaluation, and theory of this approach. This for me is the point. Many music therapists work in ways that approximate roughly to the values of CoMT (Curtis, 2015). I feel that CoMT offers a way of thinking that puts their work into a helpful perspective, regardless of whether they use the term themselves. All the same, the term is a good place to start.

What Is Community Music Therapy?

CoMT is not so much a thing you do, as a way of doing it. Most leading authors avoid providing definitions, relying instead on other modes of pointing to its key features: manifestos, lists of attributes, or case studies. I have tried to take the same approach; rather than offer a prescription of practice, I've offered my own ways of thinking and making choices. There are of course seminal examples of practice, and the increasing body of case studies generates its own implicit procedures and values. There is some comfort in this for the practitioner but also a risk. The risk is that we settle into modes that seem reliable, eye-catching, or endorsed within the body of CoMT knowledge, rather than continuing to let music show us what we can do. There will always be more to discover.

Still, there are key features by which we can recognize CoMT both in others' work and in our own thinking and practice. These have emerged out of honest and informed reflection over decades, and I feel that at this time in its development, CoMT has a distinct and valuable voice to offer. The main signatures of CoMT are found within its ecological perspective. This gives it a particular way formulating concepts of "music", "need", and "the person". These formulations affect choices every day and in each aspect of professional life. If you recognize yourself in these formulations, chances are that your work will show it or it will want to.

Ecological Perspective

CoMT has been classified as an ecological approach since at least 1998 (Bruscia, 1998). This allies the practice with a psychosocial orientation, in which music and health are seen as performed states. Along with professional practice, these aspects are seen as parts of numerous interconnected systems, each affecting the other. Whilst traditional thinking in music therapy places "the client" at the centre of these systems, modelling a classic cosmos, an ecological approach does not centre anything, insisting instead that we are all dependent on each other's movements. In this sort of decentred system, knowledge is created locally but affects everything across the system. It is both local and global, working in complex or multiple ways amongst and between us.

Consequently, CoMT theory has developed alternative ways of characterizing practice. It tends toward rethinking the causal individualism of the medical model and of positivist science. Its focus on the contextual manifestation of music and health tends to question boundaries between traditional concepts such as therapy and education, or treatment and impact. It is likely to be especially mindful of the political and ethical. The focus of CoMT is often more complex than "the individual" and harder to define. This may sometimes be simply the individual in context, with practice reflecting the local characteristics of the individual's setting. This may even, for a time, as in PJ and Caryl's examples later (Chapters Four and Five), look like standard 1:1 functional work. In other situations, it will lead to activity within more fuzzy social groupings, changing and fluid communities, or even alternative persons such as the organizations associated with "JUNK" (Chapter Six) or the social conditions of Paddy's home life (Chapter Seven). The point is that the choices about the practice have emerged out of a particular kind of thinking and are open to change and development on the basis of that thinking.

Key Signatures

Three aspects, more than any others, act as signatures of CoMT. These are the formulation of "music", "need", and the "person". I will mention them here, but Chapter Two will discuss these "key signatures" of CoMT in more detail.

Music

The understanding of "music" that seems to underpin most reporting of music therapy is that is it applied to people and has a beneficial effect on the symptoms of their individual clinical conditions. Music is assumed to have observable outcomes that can then be generalized into a patient or client's life. This approach is supported, often despite ourselves, in our choices of vocabulary or formulation of case studies, appearing throughout research literature, reinforced by the standard vocabulary of popular journalism, marketing, and PR.

In contrast with this approach, characterized by Stige and Aarø as "music as means" (2012, p. 118), CoMT proposes an alternative, systems-based understanding of music. It sees music as the co-creative manifestation of a system: as itself the "milieu" (Stige & Aarø, 2012, p. 119) in which it operates. In CoMT, music is decentred, because all the elements making it are themselves decentred. It is itself contextual, its own praxis.

Need

Music therapy accounts are normally related to our professional classification of "need". The process of reporting is a translation from co-created aesthetic experience into highly specialised professional concepts. Those concepts take on the effect of rhetoric and jargon by repetition across our profession. Our music therapy reports tend to describe a person in terms of what they might "need" from us, and then we describe how music meets that need—or not. The standard way of doing that is to focus on individual clinical symptoms, as described medically. We then focus our reports on how music effects or impacts upon those clinical symptoms.

CoMT adopts a wider view of need. It does this in two ways. First, it may take notions of social, political, or artistic "need" into account. It may identify that the deficit in a situation may not be only physiological or chemical, but also systemic, and therefore it may require a systemic response. Second, it may reject the notion of "need" altogether. In examples such as Rolvsjord's work on resource-oriented music therapy (2010), we see a parallel of CoMT responding to a person's resources, abilities, and upward potential, instead of their apparent lack thereof.

The Person

Consistent with this alternative view of "need" is the expanded notion of the "person" associated with CoMT. The dominant view in standard music therapy is that music, addressed to specific needs, takes place in one person, boundaried and autonomously defined. This is most obvious in experimental research studies that focus on chemical or symptomatic change. It is implicit in psychosocial research that looks at behavioural impact or aspects such as consumer identity. The emerging topic of music therapy in mass culture and social media is a grey area.

CoMT takes a broad view of who a "person" is, in the sense that personhood is seen as performative and thus contingent on circumstances. Following this, CoMT reframes the concept of "the client" not only so that it can include more people, that is, wider groups or social interests; it also assumes that "persons" might include other types of legal persons, too. A significant stakeholder or beneficiary in the wider ecology of practice may well be a company, charity, or constituency of people. This adds complexity to professional thinking and is a warning about following where "people and music lead". Personhood in CoMT is understood to be a performance in the sense that it is co-created out of the particular conditions of a context.

Matrix Thinking

This view of CoMT presents an approach that offers an open and systemic stance on music, on therapeutic need, and on the person who is the focus of practice. The risk with this view is that it seems too open and so systemic as to be difficult to navigate. I will share my own thoughts on how to navigate some of this openness and on how to read some of those systemic features. I will suggest that what I call "matrix thinking" can help manage the potential of CoMT.

Matrix thinking has two main aspects. First, it sees every element in our context musically. That is, it looks from within at how each element interrelates, changes, and contributes to the wider meaning and values of the system. It leads us to think holistically but as an active participant— perhaps like a conductor or even an audience member. We hear the whole, albeit from within, and respond to how it manifests moment to moment. Second, matrix thinking is based in practice. It is thinking that comes out of doing. This means that the main aspects of matrix thinking relate to everyday choices, such as what mode of musical work is appropriate (the format), what you want to achieve (the aim), what is going on around you that might affect these choices (the context), and how you are going to eventually account for all of this professionally (the evaluation). Throughout these choices, you are affected either by your preunderstanding of theory or often also by the lack of theory to help with these practical choices. So theory matters here, too.

Formats

The term "format" denotes a way of framing and structuring a music therapy encounter. It describes the "visible" part of our work: what it looks like and what it says about its cultural situation. It also more implicitly describes the inner motivation for activity, engaging with the person and the context either to enhance or indeed to challenge their expectations. Across the studies in this book, I will describe individual improvisational formats, 1:1 tuition and composition, small groups, workshops, bands, concerts, trips, rehearsals, joint sessions, family times, community singing times, corporate events, community arts projects, and college courses. The way we characterize our practice in formats emerges from an engagement with the person involved. It is not imposed by our own preunderstanding, although it is informed by our resources, skills, and experience.

Aims

Naturally, when your formats of practice are so varied, your aims within those formats will vary, too. Individual transformation matters in CoMT. That can often best happen within functionally derived individual formats of practice. In those and other circumstances, the notion of setting aims makes sense. In other types of CoMT, that notion is incongruent and can cut across the artistic or social flow of the work. Sometimes it is important, for the sake of reporting, that your practice can be translated into the language of aims and outcomes, but this is still a performance. In many music therapy moments, our aims during playing are musical and only musical terms can describe them. Aiming is always balanced by a more open artistic stance of allowing things to happen, for their own sake.

Context

I understand context not only in terms of the people and places surrounding the client. A multiplicity of formats and aims generates a huge range of interested parties, stakeholders, values, and modes of communication. These elements come together to create a large list of potential discourses running through and around your practice. My approach to managing this is to think about the matrix of discourses that construct my context at any given moment. In Chapter Six, I will describe the matrix of discourses in a large care home company and music therapy charity, identifying 17 discourses that could have been active in co-constructing the context of my work. The professional music therapy discourse is one of those, and many choices may come from that line, but it is not the only discourse at play and it will be affected by the many others that surround and connect with it.

Evaluation

The layers of formats, aims, and contextual elements in CoMT then present a challenge in making informed choices, documenting them, and evaluating the process. This approach presents multiple beneficial outcomes or impacts, and its wide range of stakeholders can generate a similarly wide range of evaluative purposes. Reflexive practice is both informal and formal, contained in numerous practical and intellectual structures. In Chapter Seven, I will share a starting point for matrix thinking around evaluation, including a practical tool and some discursive thoughts on the topic.

Theory

The language I use here to discuss matrix thinking in CoMT employs a small number of important words. Those include "emergence", "complex", and "performative". The theory of CoMT is interwoven with practice by its nature, so it is not given a separate chapter in this book. Instead it is treated as part of the practice, but it all the same requires specific technical understanding if it is going to develop further. There is a particular need for us to find new ways of talking about the simultaneous manifesting of the person, music, and context that is the hallmark of matrix thinking. This holds a rich seam of insight for music therapy generally and is one of the main contributions that CoMT can make to our discipline. It is possible that an enhanced concept of emergence, complexity, and performativity will be central parts of our theory in the coming years.

Creating a Matrix

How, then, to think about a music therapy approach in which change is characterised as emergent, complex, and performative? How do we formalise what to do and why we do it? How can we give value to what has happened when we have done it? One way, which is what I will suggest here, is to accept this emergence, complexity, and performativity as an advantage, not a problem. This involves us dropping the desire for linear, causal protocols (if *this*, then *that*) and developing alternative, multiple models of practice. "Multiple" here does not mean diverse, but instead refers to models that factor in unpredictability and provide for that within their structures. Rather than a mental attitude that applies music to a situation of need, it involves adopting a view that allows the musical structures of your encounters to manifest themselves. For this to have a formal safety net, we need to see the picture as fully as possible, presented to you as if in one go. We need to see everything in relation to everything else, musically, organized on equal terms: the matrix of music.

A matrix, according to the *OED*, is a type of structural environment. Culturally, it can refer to a social or political environment in which something develops. In geology or biology, it is a structure in which gems, crystals, or other substances are embedded. The world of printing uses a matrix as a mould in which something, such as a record or printing type, is cast. For mathematicians, a matrix is a rectangular array of quantities or expressions in rows and columns that is treated as a single entity and manipulated according to particular rules. Finally, readers who are part of large organizations may well recognize the term to mean an organizational structure in which two or more lines of command, responsibility, or communication may run through the same individual.

I am intrigued by all these resonances: music therapy as a practical environment in which a person could flourish and develop; music as a structure in which points of personal contact or emergence were embedded, like gems in a rock; a music therapy program as an aesthetic organizational structure in which a person's recovery could be cast or shaped; a music therapy evaluation as an array of quantities or expressions that is seen as a whole, yet complex, single entity; and the role of the music therapist as one in which multiple lines of thought, communication, and persona might flow as needed. Finally, of course, the clear image of the matrix as a place of birth, or rebirth, resonates on many levels within the arts, in terms of recovery, adjustment to illness or disability, and use in processes of therapy.

For me, the matrix structure has two attractive aspects. First, there is a philosophical point about seeing every structural element in our work as a musical element. This does not mean that you should think of how any element can be turned into a song, nor is it just a poetic device. Instead it draws on the way in which some neurologists, philosophers, and sociologists describe things using the matrix of music as a metaphor: That is, they see neural or social organization each as being in constantly renewing meaningful interrelation on multiple levels. This would say that in CoMT, "everything is music". The orders, types, and reach of impact can be thought of musically by seeing them all in constant reorganization with each other. This way of thinking requires us to stand back and look at how all the elements such as materials, people, formal programs, identity, and, of course, sound, interrelate, how they co-create one another, and how the meaning of our work is made in their interrelation. That field of vision is not limited to a treatment room or a dyadic encounter. It can span the whole cultural field of a community and reach into the political ends of citizenship or social justice.

Following this, the second aspect is to start and end with practice. What we know about our work is really manifest in what we do and how we do it. A matrix approach is fundamentally practice-based. It works on the idea that we choose what to do mainly by looking at what a person or a situation needs and what music can afford. Checked against professional, ethical, and practical limitations, we proceed freely toward the optimum musical experience to meet those needs. It suggests that the success of a program or a session is mostly down to the strategic choices we make and the rightness of our skills and techniques. In doing, and on reflecting, we build a theory to check and explain our action. "Music" then comes to describe both the material of the matrix (how we organize what we play and do) and what the matrix contains or releases (what we play and do itself).

We are exploring a music therapy approach built on a decentred understanding of music, need, people, and practice. I will be offering a way of formalising this using an integrative model I call the "matrix". This matrix thinking will explore "FACETs" of CoMT, including formats, aims, context, evaluation, and theory. We will touch on new aspects of theory, using examples from nature such as the emergent properties of slime mold and the rhizomic structures of tubers and bulbs. Finally, we will ourselves emerge with new directions for further thought, most prominently around emergence, complexity, and performativity. Our companions will be four wonderful people on illuminating music therapy journeys.

Here I recall a moment with our first companion, PJ (Chapter 4), sitting as she was: in a neuro-rehab treatment room, amongst a pile of household objects, discarded gardening tools, percussion and nursing equipment, ready to make music with them all. I remember how she looked around herself in wonder, drawing from everywhere to make sounds in improvisation, and asked, "How is *everything* music?"

Chapter 2

THE MUSIC MATRIX

"Everything Is Music"

Here we pause to consider the idea that "everything is music". I will suggest that it is not only musicians and poets, or PJ, for whom this notion is intuitively right. It is becoming more than metaphor for thinkers, researchers, and practitioners from many diverse fields. Far from being limited to coded texts on manuscripts or even to organized sounds, music is increasingly being viewed as an organising principle of life. What makes something music, or musical, is complex organization across material, semantic, symbolic, and social domains. The order, type, and reach of this organization are multiple. In this way, music is a matrix for action, as well as often being the sounds of that action coming into being. Music, as a mode of organization, is a matrix for how we make sense of the world; it is also how the world hangs together independently of us, our ears, or indeed our piano hands.

The way we meet the world is musical; the way the world offers itself up to be met is musical, too. We experience that meeting in countless different ways, most of which we wouldn't normally call "music". All the same, the world makes sense to us because of things we can only use musical understanding to describe. Over the last century, a polyphony that includes (amongst others) psychoanalysts, child development specialists, neurologists, evolutionary psychologists, sociologists, and philosophers has caught up with what poets and mystics have said for much longer: Music is how we know we are alive. When Rumi famously said, "We have fallen into the place where everything is music", he wasn't talking only about a mystical state of union. He was talking about just being human.

Our starting point is that "everything is music". Perhaps, I like to imagine, a young student stops Rumi right there and says, *"Wait a second, Master. Everything? How is this cup I am holding, "music"? How is this circle we are sitting in, "music"?"* Sensing a positivist, Rumi sighs, mentally filing the rest of his poem temporarily. Perhaps Rumi (here in the voice of a clumsy Englishman) replies,

"First, well done for sensing that pause in my poem and for jumping in so quickly yet somehow politely. Well done also, for so elegantly reaching out to exactly where that cup was and for coordinating your fingers so expertly around it, bringing it just so to your lips without cracking a tooth. And how naturally we all seemed to arrive and organise ourselves into this circle, silencing ourselves without being shushed, spaced as we are periodically and evenly, regularly almost. And do you feel the growing anticipation that I do, at wondering what will happen next?"

"Uh, yeah ..."

"Well, now ..."

He does not, although he might, quote Stern's Vitality Affects (1985), Malloch and Trevarthen's Communicative Musicality (2009), or Pavlicevic's Dynamic Form (1997). Nor does he feel the need to bring in his Quantum Physics or Deleuze on Creativity. But if he had, he would have only supported his observation on the musicality of human life.

One question we could go on to vex ourselves with is, "What is music?" This is a fair question, and one that my imagined Rumi conveniently avoids answering except by saying, *"everything is"*. Another perhaps more pertinent question is, "How does music manifest?" How does music makes itself known? This question points to the meeting between the world and us. This is where music is and how it manifests. Being, as we are, part of the world, music manifests in us as we make sense of everything. Musicality is our best way of explaining how we make meaning in the material and symbolic world.

For some, this manifests in ideas about how mothers and infants interact. For others, in how the brain works. Others see it in how people create social life and from that create culture. Musicality is how we structure the world, and very often music is what those structures then produce. Music is, to paraphrase Seamus Heaney's poem "Markings", both the gate and what comes through it. In this way, in structuring how we are together and being what we do, music provides a matrix of action (DeNora, 2000). This manifests on a cellular level, shown by music therapy studies in immunology or neurology (Altenmüller et al., 2009). It happens symbolically in the dynamics of interaction and self-knowledge (Stern, 1985) and becomes a force of social life and culture (Ansdell & DeNora, 2016). Music is manifest in how the structural parts of life come together and very often also in the actual sounds that are produced from that organising of parts. It is the sign of those parts working well enough together. As we know, this is what makes it so deliciously useful as therapy.

Before we get sidetracked by asking "What is music therapy?", important and interesting as that question might be, let's ask this: "How is music therapy manifest?" What is manifest when music is used systematically within a specific professional frame for the benefit of others? (Darnit, there, I did it … pretend you didn't see it.) In what structures is music's beneficial property active and knowable? As a music therapist, if you are working on interaction, you will encounter it in the pauses, interjections, and exchanges of communication. If, say, you are looking at fine and gross motor skills, you might note it in the way a person reaches out and takes a beater or indeed a cup. If social life is your focus, you may find the beneficial power of music in how people are motivated to come to a group or self-organise or in how one person has the confidence momentarily to interject with an awkward question. There will be moments when such manifestations of music therapy occur simultaneously, unpredictably, or seemingly along with your actions, rather than as a result of them. Music therapy is a peculiar flowering, very often being the gate for beneficial change, and of course what then comes through into audible and visible action.

We might say that music therapy is manifest both in the structural features of how it is made to happen and also in the sights and sounds that are produced when it is done. The underlying matrix for this is our interactions, coordinated movements, and social organization: which we know musically. Sometimes the outputs of that matrix come in the form of sounds made purposefully by instruments or voices, but not always. In music therapy, everything really is music, whether you can hear it or not. There is no essential distinction between what you can do in music and what you can do in music therapy. There will be circumstantial, ethical, or theoretical distinctions, of course. But those we impose on ourselves and on each other.

Not every approach to music therapy takes this line. CoMT is a recent example of a music therapy subdivision that explicitly encompasses within its range of therapeutic activities anything that can be done in music. More precisely, its theoretical formulation starts from what is done in music and what that affords those who are doing it. In theory, music therapy activities are then chosen and adapted out of what music affords beneficially in a given situation. The observable benefits of that choice may manifest in multiple ways, according to who is doing and who is observing.

"FACETs" of Music

The heart of CoMT is that music is multifaceted. CoMT's influence over the last decade has been mostly to open up the conversation on how the social aspect works as one of those facets, but it is not limited to that. In my take on CoMT, the whole world of music is as layered and open for beneficial use as a world is possible to be. Our own literature, joined with studies from fields such as neurology, medicine, endocrinology, sociology, and cultural studies, illuminates a "world of experience" that ranges from the biochemical to the mass cultural often in the same musical moment.

Why is this important? Imagine this: You are improvising in a music therapy group with a lady who, whilst living with a life-limiting condition, is still aware and reflective enough to know she is part of something—even if that "something" were shared only with you. In her singing or playing, you see her change; perhaps she grows flushed with excitement, her movements or articulation are more fluent, she becomes more confident, or she shows pleasure in recognizing a familiar tune.

We can posit fairly confidently from standard and CoMT literature that the event of your musicing with her is impacting across a range from the chemical to the cultural. Your shared musical experience will be manifesting in her biochemistry, neural organization, vital signs, attention, will, emotions, physical coordination, interpersonal relating, social identity, and cultural orientation. It will also be manifesting similarly within and amongst the family, friends, staff, and organization of the setting in which you are working. Because you are part of that setting, it is doing exactly the same thing in you.

Musical organization, in that moment, is manifest not only in the elements we usually call "musical": tone, pulse, rhythm, harmony. Nor is it manifest only in the person we focus on as the "client" or name as the recipient of our attention. It is manifest simultaneously in each of us: in our chemical composition, our brain cells, our heartbeat, our psychological state, our modes of personal relating, and our social and cultural identity. We can see all of these as musical structures, as they are material for musical change when we are playing.

Yet if music is, as Stige (2002) writes, "incredibly multifaceted" (p. 49), it would help us to have a way of understanding its complexity. The next section traces my way of making sense of music's bewildering range of impact. There are elements in this range of impact that don't easily fit together. Knowledge about music's "effect" on hormonal change, derived as it is from medical studies, can read uncomfortably if you understand the world from a more sociopolitical point of view. Similarly, cultural studies of how music works in everyday life can seem anecdotal or "soft" to a reader from a medical or psychological tradition. All the same, here the elements are. All together. This chapter offers no grand theory, and it doesn't attempt to reconcile elements or ideas that can't be. But it does like to bring them together.

Range of Musical Impact

Order, Type, and Reach of Impact

Back in your music therapy group, let's say in a care home, you notice that the lady is now responding to a known tune. She is moving her arms and mouthing words. Her daughter, visiting as she does during your session time, is moved physically as well as emotionally. On the periphery, you are aware of a carer; she is thrilled and surprised at what is happening. You feel the mood of the room lift. The film recording of this moment might be useful in the next staff training session you will run. You think for a second of how it might look on YouTube, but you don't go there. Years later, you meet a nurse who had attended one of your training sessions at the time. She tells you that seeing your film made her think differently about dementia care. It improved her work. She thanks you.

Such a lot happens when we make music in that sort-of-private, sort-of-public situation, where bodies physical, professional, and politic combine. In CoMT, we attune to that broad range of possibilities for two reasons: first, because it represents the widest possible chance of benefit to the client, and second, because it feels most true to how music seems to work. It recognizes that music impacts in the moment, across a huge range of elements, and that it impacts over time, through a wide range of processes. I think of this in terms of the "order", the "type", and the "reach" of impact.

"Order"

Musical change happens across elements that have differing properties, or "order". That is, change can be manifest in the material of the physical body and also in the structures of personal relating, in the fabric of social, political, or cultural identity, and simultaneously in the conditions of the surrounding environment. Whilst music therapy can impact on elements of a biological order, in the same moment it can influence aspects that are less concrete, such as professional standards or organizational expectations. These are musicalized elements, too, but of a different order than the physical body. Embracing the possibility of beneficial change in all orders of being, from chemical to cultural, CoMT attunes us to how musical experience is manifest via different material forces at the same time.

"Type"

There are different "types" of change, too. The most important type of change is of course a beneficial impact upon the person or people at the heart of the work. When we see someone alter physically, resolve or emerge emotionally, or connect socially, we feel perhaps on our most solid ground. However, we can also be party to other types of outcome. Social or political representation, advocacy, and consciousness-raising are other important ways in which music therapy impacts on situations. In some cases, the beneficial outcome is accompanied by an increase in visibility for artistic processes or music therapy professional values within an organization. It is also likely that commercial values can be implicated in our work, especially within private companies or public charities. That type of change is not our reason for being here, but it matters all the same. Being clear about the "type" of change matters because it demonstrates what your eyes and ears have been attending to and what matters to the people you work with. It matters particularly when your approach is open to more than one type of outcome or to a number of different workplace agendas.

"Reach"

The "reach" of CoMT is potentially greater than in many other approaches, because it incorporates the public and participatory in its formulation. This orientation toward the benefits opened up by witnessing a person in music tends naturally toward the option of public showings, recordings, concert projects, or creative approaches to dissemination. In some ways, CoMT can offer a wider reach of impact, both geographically and in terms of participant numbers, but this can also be a risk. CoMT literature suggests that a person can benefit from having their musical work witnessed by others or from being more directly in a social or political frame at certain times; it does not suggest that this is always the right move. Nor is it an automatic justification for digital recording and dissemination of sound or images by social media. It is better to think of CoMT as an approach that has the option, but not the unbridled imperative, of "following where people and music lead" (Pavlicevic & Ansdell, 2004, p. 30).

Musical Formats

Along with Pavlicevic and Ansdell (2004), I have come to use the term "formats" to denote the different ways in which I was following people and music. The thinking goes that since the matrix model was based in a common operation of music, all kinds of music-making could in theory become avenues for music therapy. If it were part of a coherent and safe practical approach, a music therapist could identify the most appropriate kind of music therapy encounter for their client and know that their musical work was part of an interconnected program of musical possibilities that had its own safety and rigour.

The term "format" has come to denote a way of framing and structuring a music therapy encounter. This would almost certainly include individual improvisation and group improvisation, but increasingly in my work (and in numerous others' work, too), it has come to include things like large, open, drop-in sessions, specialist tuition, ongoing ensembles such as rock bands or choirs, and supported musical workshops. It seems important to stop and think at this point, because a new format not only denotes a new set of aims or a new context. It necessarily involves addressing a new set of evaluation criteria, leading to new expectations, cultural assumptions, and even possibly a new persona as a practitioner. As a reflexive practitioner, this leads to new theory, too. An openness to the order, type, and reach of music tends to a more open perspective on the facets of music therapy.

Music Is Multimodal

This thinking is certainly not unique. It is reflected in a widespread movement in music therapy that features a number of new models or theoretical perspectives, including ecological music therapy (Ruud, 1998), culture-centred music therapy (Stige, 2002), resource-oriented music therapy (Rolvsjord, 2010), and music-centred music therapy (Aigen, 2005). It is specifically allied to the music-centred approach pioneered by Nordoff and Robbins (1974) and to the diverse area of practice that has become known as CoMT (Pavlicevic & Ansdell, 2004). One way to make connections between these approaches is to link them with what Stige (2002) calls a more "*integrative* conception" (p. 19) of selfhood. In this conception, a person is not constructed autonomously in concentric circles ranging from the local to the universal, but through a system of relationships between the many shared aspects of selfhood, including the biological, social, psychological, transcendent, and cultural.

The integrative model of selfhood and society is important because it reflects how we construct music. Music, like selfhood and society, is multimodal. It is talked about in so many different ways and through so many different discourses. Music is the subject of neurology, psychology, education, sociology, spirituality, biomedical theory, and health care, not to mention musicology, critical theory, philosophy, cultural studies, and performance. One reason that music sometimes feels limited in music therapy is that we can feel forced into isolating our theoretical understanding to one field of knowledge. Rather than look to an outside field of knowledge to explain practice, the matrix model follows other approaches to music therapy in reframing music itself as the point of connection, and also the evidence, of its knowledge system. But what do these different discourses say about music? How do they use it? Two examples, neuromusicology and music sociology, have been useful in the development of this way of thinking. I have found that writers in both fields conceive of music in similar terms: that it works in and between us as a comparable way of organising—not as a function, an affect or an object.

Altenmüller (2004) describes how music works both in our individual lives and also "in the organization of community life and in the forging of connections amongst members" (p. 26). In music, the modes of individual and social cannot truly be separated. He critiques his own tradition when he writes that in neurology, music has long been studied in isolation (i.e., in the laboratory), not amongst people in their everyday settings. Laboratory experiments in the past have attempted to isolate functions associated with music, such as code recognition or physical memory, but in doing so may have missed what he considers the "real music". He suggests that a person's "real music" would be quite different from what has been observed under laboratory conditions:

> In summary, as soon as we consider "real music" apart from laboratory experiments, we have to expect individually formed and quickly adaptive brain substrates, including widely distributed neuronal networks in both hemispheres. In our laboratories, we are just beginning to face the enormous challenges linked to the clarification of rules determining this puzzling variety of findings, determining the complexity and transitoriness of neuronal interactions during music processing. (Altenmüller, 2003, p. 352)

In other words, "real music" is music made in regular settings, that is, in practice, amongst people. "Real music" draws on widespread parts of the brain, in complex and unpredictable ways and in ways that are adapted to each individual in their context.

Although music is seen in neurology to be local and personal, it is also considered to be universal: not because everyone in the world makes pieces of music, but because we all operate musically (Altenmüller, 2004; Munte, Altenmüller, & Janke, 2002; Peretz & Zatorre, 2003; Turner & Ioannides, 2009). If there is something universal about music, it is a common capacity for musicality, rather than similarities or commonalities amongst our music practices. In other words, music is universal by virtue of *the way* it is made out of the connected operations within and amongst us rather than *what* is made. Similarly, Cross (2001a) writes that music is "universal yet multifarious" in that it is common to all, interdependently created, and simultaneously experienced individually.

The consensus in neuromusicology suggests that music is not simply another function—it does not have a "centre" in the brain—but instead a varying and overlapping set of neuronal relationships which create a matrix, drawing together multiple and varied functions or operations. It is this decentred organising that characterizes something as music. A key influence on this view is the idea of *modularity* (e.g., Peretz & Zatorre, 2003). In this concept, the different parts of music are processed in not only different parts of the brain but also in different levels, creating separated, overlapping, and interrelated patterns. Musical operations within people are considered to be *both* independent *and* interdependent.

They both create, and are created by, the connections between parts of the brain. They occur in the many actions we associate with music, including playing, singing, listening, and dancing (Cross, 2001b) and provide the basis for social interaction.

On a social level, explored here within a sociological discourse, the operation of music between and amongst us is to create, and be created by, the lived connections between people. Whilst neuromusicology helps to explain how music structures individual action, music sociology shows how it structures our shared social organization, ideas, or experience in similar ways. Music sociologist Tia DeNora describes social life itself as a web within which music is a formative feature. She writes that for individuals, "music provides a basis or reckoning, an animating force or flow of energy, feeling, desire, and aesthetic sensibility that is action's matrix" (2000, p. 152).

Music provides this matrix for human action through the properties—or in DeNora's term, "affordances" (2000, p. 39)—it holds. This marks an exciting shift away from concerns about what music is *about* to what it *makes possible:* "And, depending on how it is conceptualised, the concept of "affordance" highlights music's potential as an organising medium, as something that helps to structure such things as styles of consciousness, ideas, or modes of embodiment." (2003, p. 46). This property of human structuring creates community in the same flow of organization that individual brains use to create inner meaning.

To stand back, therefore, and look at the whole picture, is very difficult. It is not possible when choosing a course of action or a mode of evaluation to account for how music works from every possible angle. The human reality is that whilst music may have many facets, we have (at most) two hands and one head. The dizzying sum of music's potential in the end has to be delivered by one person, at one time. So we need a way of looking and thinking that can translate between that multiple, complexifying world of musical experience and the concrete, unifying actions of the everyday. Matrix thinking allows you to take a perspective that sees the whole as more than the sum of its parts, mediating the individual and the social or communal in one moment.

Application in Music Therapy

In music therapy accounts dating back to the 1960s (Dickerson, 1982; Odell-Miller, 1995; Pavlicevic & Ansdell, 2004; Pickett, 1976; Stige et al.,

2010; Tyson, 1968), music is described as something that mediates the relationship between individuals and communities. These accounts acknowledge that for each person, music therapy incorporates "inner", and also "social", processes in one functional act. We have more recently been opened up to the connections between the individual, inner world or functioning of a person and their social or "political" life (Procter, 2006; Rolvsjord, 2010). In recent music therapy literature, "community" has been used as a term that also refers to political status or citizenship (Curtis, 2012; Curtis and Sigmon Mercado, 2004). This again derives from an understanding of music as something that mediates the individual and group. Ansdell (in Kenny & Stige, 2002) relates this in the following way:

> The main agenda of Community Music has been the re-creation of community by providing opportunities for musical participation. ... The discourse is often a social and political one, setting an agenda for work with geographically—or socially defined groups who suffer marginalization. ... An important strand of this thinking considers how the individual and the group relate in contemporary society, and what role music-making has in the changing relationship between them.
> (Ansdell, 2002, p. 116)

The musical structures that create and also result from the interplay between the individual and the group are the tools of our trade. In practice, our challenge is to find a way of using these tools in a safe and effective way. In practice, three principles are central to the way these tools are used safely and effectively. They are:

- All music therapy formats make use of the common properties of music.

- Participants do not necessarily follow a single linear route from one format to the next, and some participants can be engaged with several formats in the same program.

- The music therapist needs to oversee all the formats in a music therapy program.

The matrix approach is not prescriptive and thus does not set out any ideal model of development or treatment. This means that one person's trajectory from individual music therapy to a small group and then to a workshop course could signal important rehabilitative progress, but conversely, for another person, progress might be represented by a trajectory in the opposite direction. All would depend on circumstances: how referrals or contact happened, on resources, and on dependency or need. Does this approach require us to change as music therapists? Does it demand an expansion of music therapy skills? Are people doing this already? The answer to each of those questions is: "Probably yes". In 2006, I identified a list of skills that had become important to this approach to music therapy practice. I suspected that they are in fact common amongst music therapists, but that some are perhaps less valued or practised. The list was as follows:

- Using improvisation, and repertoire with an improvisational attitude.
- Accompanying.
- Working with a learning focus.
- Thinking ahead into the program: planning courses, etc.
- Facilitating a workshop led by someone else.
- Training/choosing workshop leaders.
- Structuring sessions.
- Creating appropriate performance opportunities.
- Collaborating with other agencies, for example, media, social services, local arts bodies, churches, community venues.
  (Wood, 2006, retrieved online)

For some people, these would seem an obvious part of their skill set. To others, some may appear antithetical to the work of a music therapist. None of them stands alone, however. Each one is seen as the manifestation of a musical form that has individual significance for a person within the context of a wider system. That system will be different for everyone, so the formats and requisite skills will also manifest differently in each situation. Indeed, we manifest just as contingently as our clients and their situation.

In CoMT, it is therefore very difficult to speak of the "I" of the therapist, or of the "him/her" of the client. Indeed, it is also hard to speak meaningfully of the "it" of music. Matrix thinking is a more complex approach, seeing that in our music-making, "I" and "you" and "it" also manifest irreducibly as "we". Not so much merged, however, as fractal. In the section below, I will suggest that we are all elements in a bigger system that can be understood only via a new set of concepts. These new concepts don't break the parts into smaller details, but they help us to stand back, look again, and accept that our work is more than the sum of its parts.

Multiplicity

Here is a matrix with which most or all of us will be familiar:

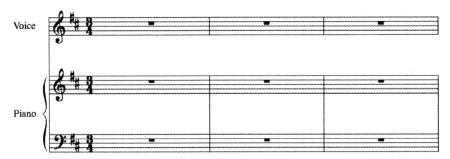

This musical score shows us a system, structured with defined features. It stays stable until we change it. It shows us the scope of the system, so in this example we can see how it comprises elements of probably two people, each playing their own line but sharing a particular kind of timing and scale. A score like this is already a matrix that enables us to stand one step back: It shows us the field with all elements laid out. We see not only one line, but all of them, spaced so that we can also note what happens between the lines as well as within them. Of course, when we fill the matrix in with values, we witness that structure come to life:

In this example, much more is presented than just the static parameters of the system. The system is shown dynamically, too: A piano melody is apparently repeated in the voice. The piano left hand is in a first inversion. The voice imitates the articulation of the piano, at once legato and then accented on the first beat. There is a picture of harmonic development, expressive interaction, and change, both within parts and between them. Perhaps when reading this you hear the sounds in your mind. You may ask questions: Is this a transcription of an improvisation? Who are the people playing this? Is it significant that the melody is repeated? Why is the piano chord a first inversion? And what happens next?

Whilst we might imagine that the person singing here is separate from the person at the piano, this matrix shows them also as part of one system. The person singing is a singer *plus* something else. Similarly, the pianist here is represented as something more than only a pianist: She is a pianist *plus* something else. The elements in this system are fractal: They are somehow separate but also together. For this system to operate, we have to conceive of each person as more than one but less than two. Similarly, this system itself comes to life only when it is decoded by you, the reader. The score itself is more than one entity, brought to life by your participation in it and its activity in you. What's more, this matrix shows movement in time. Although it is a static image, it represents through its codes and spacial relations a dynamic interrelation that unfolds. The term most commonly used to describe systems of fractal elements that emerge dynamically in our perception is "multiplicity". A musical score is a matrix that gives us an image of multiplicity.

One further aspect of multiplicity in musical scores is that every time that score is reproduced, it will be different. No amount of hyperspecific scoring by the composer will keep each new musician from manifesting that notation slightly differently from the last. That's actually one of the things we like about music. So it is with CoMT. Perhaps one of the reasons its authors avoid prescriptive formulas in writing it is that they value difference in doing it. In the next chapter, I will explore how we balance that aspect of CoMT theory with the need for stable theory signposts. How, if CoMT is not really one thing, shall we recognise it?

Chapter 3

RECOGNIZING CoMT

Formulation of CoMT

To the annoyance of many, the leading authors in CoMT (Ansdell, 2002; Pavlicevic & Ansdell, 2004; Stige & Aarø, 2012) have never provided a unitary definition of CoMT. Whilst they have produced manifestos (Ansdell, 2002), images (Pavlicevic & Ansdell, 2004) and acronyms (Stige & Aarø, 2012), there has been a significant resistance to definition amongst them. What has emerged, however, are signatures by which CoMT might be recognized. This chapter explores the signatures of CoMT and suggests how it might be formulated in relation to a standard music therapy approach.

The formulation of CoMT influencing this book is based on an alternative perspective on the three key factors of music, need, and the person. It is grounded in accounts of practice from within the UK, Skandinavia, the US, Canada, and South Africa, with a growing and increasingly recognizable tradition of literature from those places (Stige & Aarø, 2012; Stige et al., 2010). Since many practitioners may hold to the theoretical approach of CoMT without formally adopting the title (Curtis, 2015), it seems important to use the underlying stance of CoMT as its main signifier. I understand the underlying stance of CoMT as an "ecological" approach.

The Ecological Perspective

CoMT has been classified as an ecological approach to music therapy (Bruscia, 1998):

> The ecological area of practice includes all applications of music and music therapy where the primary focus is in promoting health within and between various layers of the sociocultural community and/or physical environment.

> This includes all work which focuses on the family, workplace, community, society, culture or physical environment. (p. 229)

The ecological approach assumes that in musical experience the person can be formulated as both individual and communal and that music itself is also similarly multivalent, being manifest both in the individual and in the collective milieu in which it is situated (Stige & Aarø, 2012). Music is understood to be a site of experience rather than purely a means of prompting outcomes. Consequently, the notion of music therapy need, that is, the reason for working with the person, is drawn widely to include potential communal or social influences in addition to change in autonomous physical or psychological symptoms. An ecological approach suggests that in music therapy, "outcomes" are not necessarily derived from a process of cause and effect.

The ecological underpinnings of CoMT are allied with a psychosocial orientation, characterising music, and health, as performed states that reflect and impact upon the systems in which they are situated (Ruud, 2010; Stige et al., 2010). Those systems are a complex network of changing interpersonal, professional, and sociocultural connections. Traditional thinking in music therapy has placed the person (i.e., the "client") at the centre of a variety of settings, whether that has been within a dyad, a physical space, a family or group, or a wider social setting. An ecological approach to music therapy does not primarily centre the person, but instead accepts that the milieu in which the music therapy occurs is a changing, decentred system. That system is contingent, and alters when changes occur in any parts of the system (Kenny, 1982, 1985, 1989, 1999; Ruud, 1987/1990, 2010). An ecological epistemology suggests that knowledge is created locally, out of a changing set of factors. As context changes, so do the conditions in which knowledge is generated. An "ecological" approach positions the person—and indeed all elements around the person—within a complex system of interaction. Within this approach, personhood is assumed to be neither solely individual nor communal, but instead to be on a continuum between individual and communal.

Theoretical Framework

The theoretical framework relating to CoMT used in this book is built upon an emerging body of literature initiated principally by Stige (1993) and taken up later in the UK by Ansdell and Pavlicevic in 2004. That heritage is used as a starting point here because it expresses a unique theoretical point of view in relation to the professional implications of an ecological approach. That point of view is taken as the basis of the understanding of the term used in this book. An early articulation of this approach to CoMT came in an essay by Ansdell in 2002. Here, he provided a manifesto on a new approach to music therapy theory. It is quoted below in full:

> *Community Music Therapy* is an approach to working musically with people *in context:* acknowledging the social and cultural factors of their health, illness, relationships, and musics. It reflects the essentially communal reality of musicing and is a response both to overly individualized treatment models and to the isolation people often experience within society. In practice, *Community Music Therapy* encourages Music Therapists to think of their work as taking place along a continuum ranging from the individual to the communal. The aim is to help clients access a variety of musical situations, and to accompany them as they move between "therapy" and wider social contexts of musicing.
>
> As such, *Community Music Therapy* involves extending the role, aims, and possible sites of work for music therapists— not just transporting conventional Music Therapy approaches into communal settings. This will involve rethinking not only the relationship between the individual and the communal in Music Therapy, but also taking into account how physical surroundings, client preferences, and cultural contexts shape the work.
>
> *Community Music Therapy* aims to develop theory consistent with its view of musicing as an engaged social and cultural practice and as a natural agent of health promotion. (Ansdell, 2002, retrieved online)

In subsequent papers (2005) and discussions (2006), Ansdell developed the formulation of this new direction in music therapy theory, including, most importantly a theoretical justification for the inclusion of practices associated with education, public performance, and community music into the UK's professional remit of music therapy work. This formulation provided a way to orientate music-centred music therapy away from what he characterised as a limiting professional consensus about strictly boundaried practice into an exploration of how the profession might be enhanced by seeing music and its participants as co-creative and active in themselves directing the focus of practice. In other words, he wrote of following "where people and music lead" (Pavlicevic & Ansdell, 2004, p. 30). The articulation, with Pavlicevic, of this alternative orientation was underpinned by the use of a number of theoretical devices, notably what they refer to as "Wood's Matrix", the "Ripple Effect", and the "Individual-Communal Continuum" (Pavlicevic & Ansdell, 2004).

In later publications, this formulation of CoMT has tended to be identified by reference to elements such as performance events (meaning public showings of musical work). Maratos (2004), for instance, describes a performance project within a mental health setting that she allies with CoMT by virtue of its institutional involvement and its nontraditional use of writing and performing formats. In his foreword to Pavlicevic and Ansdell's book *Community Music Therapy,* Ruud (2004) also gives a definition of CoMT that considers musical performance as an adjunct to a systemic approach to music therapy. Turry (2005) also provides an account of what could be viewed as CoMT, citing the musical performance events as central to his work with "Maria". Connections between CoMT and theatre have been explored recently in Brandalise (2015).

All the same, CoMT resists definition by specific practices such as public musical showings. This resistance was articulated early in Ansdell's formulations, when he described CoMT as an "antimodel" (2003, p. 21). Instead it proposes an alternative stance in which context-led practice remains *a priori,* with theory continuing to be built upon experience. It is a formulation that provides theoretical orientations without being prescriptive. This resistive stance against a unifying theory is noted by Stige and Aarø (2012). Here the authors set out examples of practice and theory that can be characterized together as reflecting CoMT, without them presenting a prescriptive definition. Rather than identifying or defining CoMT, the authors characterize examples of such practice and make connections between those examples.

Stige and Aarø's recent approach is built on Stige's early work (2002, 2003), in which he offered a version of CoMT that is influenced by an engagement with context and what that means for music therapy choices and values. He put forward a notion of CoMT as: "[M]usic therapy practices that are linked to the local communities in which clients live and therapists work, and/or to communities of interest" (2002, p. 328). The ecological (or what they refer to as "systemic" below) dimensions of music therapy practice are a foundational part of Pavlicevic and Ansdell's formulation of CoMT:

> Music therapists are increasingly more often working with whole communities. They not only work with individual problems, but also focus on systemic interventions: how music can build networks, provide symbolic means for underprivileged individuals, or be used to empower subordinated groups. (Pavlicevic & Ansdell, 2004, p. 13)

The theoretical perspective underpinning this approach leads the authors to present a model that changes according to the context in which it is situated:

> CoMT is a different thing for different people in different places. … You can't have something which is context- and culture-sensitive but which is a "one size fits all anywhere" model. So you will not find authoritative definitions in this book—or recipes for practice, or techniques, as such. (Pavlicevic & Ansdell, 2004, p. 17)

A significant seam of CoMT work concerns the reterritorialising (and the redefining) of established music therapy practices cross-culturally. In a recent paper, Winter (2014) describes a project in which CoMT was used in Malawi to complement existing education provisions for students with disability. Pavlicevic and Fouché (2014) offer an account of CoMT in the Western Cape of South Africa. It is possible that CoMT offers a helpful framework for this sort of reframing, through its responsive stance to contextual conditions and its wide brief regarding the formats of practice.

The use of CoMT as an academic channel through which to discuss challenging ideas or practices is an important aspect of its appeal to some and its controversy to others. Ansdell (2005) writes of viewing practice "through the perspective of the evolving practice and discourse of CoMT—where aspects of the practice, theory, and ethics of performance in music therapy are currently being debated" (retrieved online). O'Grady and McFerran (2007) also acknowledge that CoMT is a vehicle for discussion:

> The discourse on CoMT has emerged partly as an attempt
> to redress the inadequacy of music therapy theory in
> explaining the cultural and context-dependent nature of its
> broad practices (O'Grady & McFerran, 2007, p. 14).

CoMT appears to be used as a device in some texts to include examples of practice and theory that previously would have remained marginalized: as a "Trojan Horse" of theory (see Ansdell, 2014b). This is a relevant aspect of how CoMT is used here, as it relates to its inherently critical performative stance. This formulation has arisen as an alternative to what its proponents might argue is a unifying, reductive stance within standard music therapy theory. It is relevant to maintain the possibility that CoMT is a device for avoiding theoretical reduction and for promoting a continual openness to debate or development. This has been evident most recently in a special issue of the *Journal of Community Music* devoted to intersections between CoMT and Community Music (Tsiris, 2014).

Critiques of CoMT

Aigen (2014, p. 149) outlines two main strands of critique of CoMT. The first strand of critique questions its theoretical origins, whilst the second objects to the need for it to be considered a subdivision of practice. Aigen points out that Ansdell's current formulation is only one expression of a term that in fact has a longer and geographically broader history. Aigen's account of this history is widely drawn, incorporating Stige and Ruud's exploration of context and community, the impact of de-institutionalised health and social care, and the increasing relevance of developments in musicology. Kenny's use of Field Theory (1996, 2006) should also be included in this list of theoretical origins. Aigen suggests that the current use of the name "CoMT" is only one of many formulations. In considering the necessity of the term, he suggests that its current formulation (which he associates primarily with Ansdell) raises objections concerning the professional impact of CoMT in the UK and Ireland and about the practical implications of that. In short, he notes that CoMT has been condemned both for being a superfluous term and for promoting unethical practice.

The ethical status of CoMT is a focus of Barrington's doctoral thesis and subsequent article in the *British Journal of Music Therapy*. Barrington (2005) suggests that within CoMT, the main evaluative measure is third-party feedback:

> Advocates of CoMT ... would like to base the "success" of
> each CoMT project on the fulfilment of the clients' needs.
> I suggest that respectability may occur through the positive
> responses to each CoMT project. Although this may be a
> by-product of the main work of music therapy and not a
> main goal of the work, it may nonetheless occur. To what
> extent a music therapy project has sought respectability for
> self-promotion and to what extent it has been gained due
> to the "success" of its work seems difficult to assess.
> (Barrington, 2005, p. 225)

Barrington (2008) asserts that CoMT is provocative, possibly destructive to the profession, and not in the client's best interests. For other examples of critiques based on professional concerns, see Edwards (2002) and Streeter (1999). Davies and Sloboda (2009), Jones (2007), and O'Grady and McFerran (2007) also discuss the professional implications of CoMT.

The critiques of CoMT raise two important dilemmas in relation to evaluation. Much of the critique described above (concerning terminology) is an objection to the use of the term: either that it is too broad to have a useful meaning or that it relates to practice that can already be included within the term "music therapy". Where a literature search offers accounts of CoMT evaluation, critics might suggest that those accounts may not detail the same types of practice or practices necessarily from the same theoretical perspectives.

The second objection relates to the professional status of practices associated with the term, such as public performance, and the use of recreational or educational models. This objection would argue that those practices currently associated with the term should not fall within music therapy and in fact might be unsafe or unethical when viewed from certain psychological perspectives. This objection also therefore questions the basis of CoMT evaluation, as it would suggest that those practices should be stopped rather than evaluated.

A prominent example of the controversy over practice is the continued debate over musical performance in CoMT. Aigen (2014) presents a number of issues regarding the inclusion of performance in CoMT from a psychodynamic perspective. He cites Baker (2013), Jampel (2006), Turry (1999), and York (2006) as examples of how music therapists have generated criteria for understanding the value of performance in music therapy or CoMT, and cites Streeter (2006) as providing a comprehensive basis for critique. Darnley-Smith (2013) uses the role of performance in CoMT theory to criticise the approach. She suggests that CoMT is a political device employed to challenge aspects of the music therapy profession and that it is based on false assumptions.

CoMT risks being stereotyped as an approach tainted by self-promotion and lack of clarity. Authors who co-opt the terminology of CoMT in their professional vocabulary risk seeming unnecessarily provocative. In most commonly presenting only the public musical showings that take place in our practice (the concert in the park, the composition project, etc.), we risk fulfilling the unfair prophesies of these stereotypes. CoMT theory is not a justification for loose ethics or random musical wickedness. It is a particular approach to understanding music, need, and the person. This approach guides music therapists in all manner of practices, from the public and innovative to the unseen and (apparently) standard.

Formulation of "Music"

The structure of standard music therapy is based on the assumption that "music" can have an effect on the symptoms of individual clinical conditions. Those symptoms are articulated as aspects of the person in therapy, for example, anxiety, pain, psychosis, or low awareness. The introduction of music into that situation of clinical need is assumed to have observable outcomes that can be generalized into the patient or client's ongoing life.

While individual improvisation remains the most common approach to music therapy, the diversity of music in music therapy has been influenced by a recent increase in the reported variety of treatment-based musical formats used in practice, although often without reference to CoMT at all. Recent reports have explored the relationship between live and recorded music, various methods of listening, approaches based in musical training or communication, and the relationship between musical and nonmusical interventions. This trend suggests that the musical activities reported even in individualist examples of music therapy are in fact considerably varied.

For example, Holmes et al. (2006) use a randomized, placebo-controlled trial with blinded observer rater to explore whether music, live or prerecorded, is effective in the treatment of apathy in subjects with moderate to severe dementia. Locke and Mudford (2010) note that music played through headphones was seen to reduce the disruptive chanting and vocalizations of a 68-year-old man who lived in a secure dementia unit. Ceccato et al. (2012) explore The Sound Training for Attention and Memory in Dementia (STAM-Dem). New diverse practices within music therapy are coming to challenge notions of music, what is "musical" about music therapy, and how music can impact upon multiple domains of life.

These examples suggest a complex approach to the role of music. They indicate that music might in some cases be reduced to hearing recorded sounds via headphones, an example that on one hand reinforces the causal, individualist perspective yet on the other is a pragmatic appropriation of a cultural musical practice into a therapy frame. The concern over what is effective about music in music therapy, and how to translate it into words, suggests that music remains undefined and not generally understood. It could be inferred that there remains a need for theoretical approaches that provide tools for understanding how music can be used widely in professional music therapy practice without being fully defined or understood.

Music as Milieu

In a significant contrast to the assumptions made about music in standard evaluation, summarized by Stige and Aarø (2012) as "music as means" (p. 118), CoMT proposes an alternative understanding of "music as milieu" (p. 119). This alternative stance assumes that in CoMT "the traditional question about how music works should be supplemented by questions on where, when, and with whom" (p. 119). Music in CoMT is central to the theoretical framework: It is often linked with the traditions of music-centred music therapy (Aigen, 2005). In a practical example, music in care homes is not limited to therapeutic encounters, even within the literature on music therapy evaluation. In care homes, it is likely to be expanded, naturally, to the practices of daily living. Music is increasingly seen as a potential caregiving resource within daily activities in care homes. This can be seen most clearly in Brown et al. (2000, 2001a, 2001b) and Götell et al. (2002, 2003, 2009). Hammar et al. (2010, 2011a, 2011b) show how music therapeutic caregiving can be an effective nursing intervention to provide people with dementia a more pleasant experience of morning care situations as it decreases resistant behaviour and increases positive emotions.

At the same time, the notion of music itself in CoMT is decentred. This is in some ways the more defining element of music within CoMT, rather than the blunt fact of its varied use. In CoMT, music is understood to be created in context, in action, and in interaction, rather than being a "thing in-itself". This approach has significant consequences for how we think about and report on the work, as it does not assume that individual effects can be attributed to the application of music on an individual. It also does not assume that music can be located in either a therapist or a participant. Instead, music is increasingly seen as a praxis that is co-constructed and locally situated. This is the strongest signature of music in CoMT.

Formulation of "Need"

Assessment and Evaluation

How do we know what someone needs in music therapy? Most commonly, need is established by assessment and evaluation processes. The standard characterization of assessment and evaluation in music therapy can refer to a number of interrelated knowledge practices. Bruscia (1987) suggests that assessment can be seen as the initial process that provides information about a client and sets out the criteria for ongoing evaluation, whilst evaluation is used to review that information in the light of the therapeutic process and to determine whether a particular strategy has been effective. This characterisation of assessment and evaluation assumes that music therapy is a process that is predictable, treatment-based, sequential, and one in which a client's experience can be represented in terms that can be objectively measured and compared.

The range of disciplines and discourses associated with CoMT increases the range of options for identifying need and targeting practice. Naess and Ruud (2007) explore multidimensional approaches within music therapy, suggesting that they now require several theoretical perspectives, ranging from empowerment theory to social cognitive approaches. O'Grady and McFerran (2007) investigate the relationship between music therapy and community music practices. Such connections bring in alternative ways of formulating criteria for assessment and evaluation.

A significant example of the broadening of theoretical perspectives and practices is the increase in attention given to the sound environment of health care. Kittay (2008) argues that the sound environment should figure as an area of attention in the same way that physical spaces and visual environments are adapted for specialist treatment centres. Kittay suggests that there is no consistent research tradition specific to this goal (see also Woodward, 2004). This development raises the question, in an echo of Maratos (2004), of whether the setting can have its own needs distinct from, if associated with, those of the individual.

According to Individual Symptomatic Need

The main approach in standard music therapy is to define need according to clinical diagnosis or pathology and to determine effectiveness according to change in symptoms or indicators of that pathology. The field of music therapy in mental health is a useful example of how symptoms are formulated for the purposes of music therapy evaluation. Numerous research papers report effectiveness of music therapy on psychiatric symptoms, recent examples including Brandes et al. (2010), Carr et al. (2012), Choi et al. (2008), Morgan et al. (2011), and Silverman (2011a). Gold et al. (2004) examine the efficacy of music therapy for children and adolescents with psychopathology. The authors suggest that evaluation of music therapy involves a specialist understanding of where need lies and of which needs can be demonstrated to have been met.

Another clinical field where this is of interest is neurological rehabilitation, as well as physical rehabilitation, where need in music therapy is evaluated according to a wide range of physical, functional, and behavioural indicators. In Weller and Baker (2011), the authors suggest that music therapy can meet need across a range of physical, psychological, cognitive, and emotional functioning within physical rehabilitation. In neurological rehabilitation, the range of potential needs and areas of treatment can be vast, ranging from swallowing to voice production and related mood states. This can be seen, for example, in Baker et al. (2005), Kim (2010), Kim and Tomaino (2008), Magee et al. (2006), Schlaug et al. (2008), Wilson et al. (2006), and Yinger and Lapointe (2012).

Sometimes need in standard music therapy is established by reference to a specified symptom associated with medical treatment. Relief of pain and anxiety during medical procedures has become a significant area of music therapy outcomes research, for example, in Karagozoglu et al. (2013), who investigated the effects of music therapy and visual imagery on chemotherapy-induced anxiety and nausea–vomiting. Eyre (2008) describes a medical music therapy clinical project in which clients were offered individual music therapy sessions whilst undergoing hemodialysis treatment in a general hospital. Other examples of evaluations of music therapy based on pain and anxiety relief can be found in Huang et al. (2010), Kristjánsdóttir and Kristjánsdóttir (2011), Mitchell and MacDonald (2006), Park and Hughes (2012), and Whitehead-Pleaux et al. (2006).

Another area in which symptoms or behavioural traits are identified within music therapy need is autism. Kim et al. (2008) investigate the effects of improvisational music therapy on joint attention behaviours in preschool children with autism. Results show significantly more and lengthier events of eye contact and turn-taking in improvisational music therapy than in play sessions. Boso et al. (2007); Hillier et al. (2012); Kern, Wakeford, and Aldridge (2007); and Lim (2010) describe evaluation of music therapy with children on the autistic spectrum, with a focus on specific related symptoms.

Symptoms of anxiety, stress, and depression associated with living in care homes are identified as key areas of need, for example, in Khan and Curtice (2011), Mohammadi et al. (2011), Mercado and Mercado (2006), and Sung et al. (2010). It is notable that a large proportion of music therapy evaluation and research is devoted to studying agitation behaviours among people living with dementia in care homes. For instance, Ledger and Baker (2007) investigate the long-term effects of group music therapy on agitation levels of people with Alzheimer's disease. For more on this, see also Ballard et al. (2009), Chan et al. (2009), Choi et al. (2009), Cohen-Mansfield et al. (2010a), Cohen-Mansfield et al. (2010b), Cooke et al. (2010), Garland et al. (2007), Gerdner (2000), Guétin et al. (2009), Hintz (2000), Ho et al. (2011), Horne-Thompson and Grocke (2008), Ledger and Baker (2007), Myskja (2005), Nair et al. (2011), Ridder (2005), Scalenghe and Murphy (2000), Tan et al. (2010), Van der Geer (2009), and Wall and Duffy (2010).

The standard approach in music therapy evaluation is to formulate evaluation criteria according to individual clinical need. In cases where context is included, it is implied as an indication of clinical need, for example, where music therapy was used with women residing in a shelter. The value of music therapy in this standard approach is formulated in relation to how the symptoms of individual clinical need have been alleviated.

According to Wider Ecological Considerations

Although CoMT is considered a subdiscipline of music therapy (Stige &

Aarø, 2012), its theoretical formulation challenges the standard notion of need in a number of significant ways. Primarily, the character and scope of CoMT imply an orientation toward, and impact on, a wider range of needs than standard evaluation traditionally has included (Ansdell, 2002; Stige, 2002). For example, in a recent theoretical paper, Vaillancourt (2012) demonstrates how CoMT can contribute to social justice. She describes CoMT as a creative approach that liberates expression, potentially empowering people of all ages, races, and statuses to build a better society. Such "needs" (if they can be formulated as such) would be difficult to evidence in individualist approaches. See also Vaillancourt (2010, 2011) and Curtis and Vaillancourt (2012).

Curtis (2012) examines the emergent trend of social justice in music therapy as evidenced across practice, research, and theory. It is reviewed from such varied perspectives as feminist music therapy, CoMT, peace activism, and participatory action research, as well as multicultural and empowerment approaches to music therapy. Rolvsjord (2006) explores music therapy as "empowerment" in relation to mental health. It is also a feature of CoMT that beneficial aspects such as "empowerment" or "social justice" cannot so easily be reduced to a sequence of assessment and evaluation. It is more likely that the beneficial "outcome" state is experienced simultaneously with the music. The same could be said of aesthetic values within CoMT (Shoshensky, 2011). The development of alternative aims for practice sets a different agenda for evaluation than standard models and presents a challenge to the established knowledge practices of assessment and evaluation.

Need may also be defined according to the shared features of a social subgroup. Whipple and Lindsey (1999), for example, describe a music therapy program that was established to empower women who have experienced domestic abuse and are temporarily residing in a shelter. Need in this case is understood according to more psychosocial circumstances rather than symptomatic dysfunction. Curtis (2000) developed a model of feminist music therapy for the empowerment of women. This model was assessed using a case study approach, specifically for its effectiveness in increasing the self-esteem of women abused by their male partners. See also Teague et al. (2006). It is notable that although the criteria in such examples are not directly clinically derived, they indicate clinical need and are reported in the terminology of individualist treatment models.

Formulation of "The Person"

Individualist Perspectives

The most common way of thinking about the person in standard music therapy is to characterize them as an autonomous individual, generally termed the "client" or "patient", with a predefined "need". This formulation leads to a treatment model in which the value of music therapy is measured according to what level of effect "it" has on the individual, according to terms understood by professionals working with that patient group or diagnosis. This approach can be seen in the majority of published reports. Effectiveness is therefore understood according to a range of factors that relate usually to an individual's clinical diagnosis, such as in Abromeit (2003), Cassidy (2009), Dureau (2005), and Stewart (2009), for example, who evaluate the "effects" of music therapy on newborns.

Music therapy does occasionally reach beyond the person identified by a clinical "need", exploring the additional potential impact on those close to patients or clients, as in O'Callaghan et al. (2013), who examine music's relevance, including preloss music therapy, for informal caregivers of people who died from cancer. This interest in how music therapy can benefit caregivers or can provide insight into more complex relationships is reflected also in Jacobsen and Wigram (2007), who use music therapy in the assessment of parenting competencies for parents of children potentially in need of care. Pasiali (2012) also addresses parent-child interaction. Gooding (2011) explores the role of music therapy in assessing social skills interventions. Nonetheless, the underlying theoretical basis of these approaches remains individualist, in that it supports a treatment model of music therapy as understood in relation to making change in individuals.

Another consideration in exploring how the person is formulated in music therapy is to note the trend in exploring chemical change in individual physiology. Suzuki et al. (2007), for example, explore music therapy–induced changes in behaviour by analyzing saliva concentrations in elderly patients with severe dementia. Suzuki et al. (2004) also investigated the effectiveness of music therapy using endocrinological and behavioural evaluations. These studies show how the combination of endocrinological measurements, behavioural evaluations, and functional assessment methods are viewed increasingly as being useful for evaluating the effects of music therapy. Such studies adopt a functional individualist approach to understanding the person.

Dementia care has a contrasting strand of research based on group intervention. The effects of group music interventions on behavioural and psychological symptoms in patients with dementia are explored in numerous evaluation reports, including Choi et al. (2009), Clair et al. (2005), Cooke et al. (2010a), Fischer-Terworth and Probst (2011), Guétin et al. (2009), Hulme et al. (2010), Ledger and Baker (2007), Lin et al. (2011), Raglio et al. (2008), Raglio et al. (2012), Takahashi and Matsushita (2006), Tuet and Lam (2006), Van de Winckel et al. (2004), and Zare et al. (2010). This is of interest because conclusions are drawn by such research regarding the value of music therapy for individuals, and derived from individualist research frameworks, on the basis of experiences they had as members of a group. It is striking that the implications of the ecological approach are reflected in some areas of general music therapy evaluation literature. Norman (2012) argues that music therapists need an assessment protocol that can provide a holistic, musical, ability-based picture whilst indicating what kind of music therapy treatment, if any, is best suited.

A contrasting aspect of personhood emerges in relation to consumerism and mass media. Consumer culture has emerged as a significant trend within music therapy literature. Baines and Danko (2010) report on a music therapy program first piloted in a community mental health clubhouse and six months later expanded to five community mental health group homes, all administrated by an accredited agency in the lower mainland of British Columbia, Canada. Baines (2000) described the predominantly song-based approach of that program and documented a "consumer evaluation" of it, concluding that the client-centred empowerment model of consumer inclusiveness described appeared to contribute significantly to the rehabilitative effect of the program. This is an interesting diversion away from the model of the person as "patient", "client", or "user" and toward a formulation of the person that is significantly more commercial or capitalist (in the sense of commodification and exchange).

Mass culture and media are also important features of this trend, as the person in music therapy might also be conceived as "viewer" or "viewed". Gooding and Gregory (2011) conduct a descriptive analysis of music therapy–related videos on YouTube. The authors suggest the need to consider ways to ensure accurate dissemination of music therapy–related information in the YouTube environment, ethical standards when posting music therapy session videos, and the possibility of creating professional standards for posting music therapy related video. This marks an interesting development in how the person is formulated within general music therapy evaluation. It raises questions concerning the assumptions of individualism and the fit between foundational values of standard music therapy and its current trends.

Ecological Perspectives

One significant feature of CoMT has been the broadening understanding of the person within the conceptual framing of music therapy. This has arisen both from theoretical developments such as Pavlicevic and Ansdell's "Individual-Communal Continuum" (2004), which questions the autonomy of the client on the level of the self, and also from music therapy accounts where organizations, groups, and communities have benefited in their own right, as "persons". This impact upon organizations, groups, and communities is in parallel to what can be seen as individual effects among their members.

The reframing of the person in their social context can be seen in the title of Curtis and Mercado's paper (2004) in which they discuss CoMT for "Citizens with Developmental Disabilities". Another notable example of this is in Maratos (2004), whose terminology suggests that clienthood can be reimagined from an organizational point of view. Her chapter "Whatever Next? Music Therapy for the Institution" points to this significant trend in CoMT theory. In Fouché and Torrance (2005), the authors discuss music therapy with an adolescent group involved in "gangsterism", drawing attention both to the individual and their social condition. A recent paper from Dennis and Rickson (2014) has made further progress in formulating benefit both for "client" and family, within the context of residential dementia care. Jampel (2011) also points out that the person can vary according to what mode of musical experience they are in. He suggests, for example, that CoMT theory has not yet addressed "who the person is" when they are performing.

Certainly this develops the notion expressed by Bruscia (1998, p. 229) that CoMT expands and complexifies the definition of "the client". It also adds to the ongoing clarifications throughout Stige et al. (2010) regarding the differences between "client", "participant", and "musician". It suggests first that those who benefit from CoMT can be not only individuals with stated "needs", but also individuals without a needs-based association (such as family members or supporters), groups of people with specific and/or unclear membership, and, in fact, any institutional, social, or cultural entity or interest.

Second, the boundary between "client" (a person with a specific professional relationship to the therapist, defined by duty of care), participant, and beneficiary is sometimes unclear. Even insofar as an individual is specifically referred through medical channels, in some cases family members or other social groupings will warrant duty of care or will manifest other types of client attributes. This is further complicated by the tendency of practitioners in CoMT to look beyond the functional/ instrumental aspects of practice even when working with people who have stated clinical or psychosocial needs. This also resonates with the notion raised in the literature that an individual is different according to the mode of musical experience they are in. Individuals and the organizations around them may alter further according to how they are part of musical experience. They are performing constantly. The exploration of performance via discourse has thrown new light on what it might mean to speak of the "performing person". There is a belief in CoMT that the person may indeed be understood and thus "performed" differently by varying audiences, according to the types of information or knowledge generated by and about them. This may well be affected by how they are in music: whether they are highly passive recipients or producing musical events in what would ordinarily be termed "performance" situations.

Summary

This chapter started from the position that CoMT resists definition, and that this is a good thing. Whilst some authors have produced manifestos, acronyms, and images, a clear, predictive definition is still not on the cards. Through recent seminal texts, however, the signatures of CoMT can be identified. CoMT is ecological. This allies it with a psychosocial approach, oriented toward versions of systems theory. Music and health are viewed as performative, multivalent, and contingent, and consequently CoMT outcomes are not necessarily considered to derive from a process of cause and effect. Critiques of CoMT tend to be based either on the validity of the term itself or on professional objections to aspects of practice. These criticisms are sometimes stoked by authors' presentational habits of discussing only the public or brief aspects of practice that is often also private and ongoing. Music is formulated within CoMT as a decentred, noncausal, co-creative process, or a "milieu". Need and action are identified in diverse ways, both functionally and in relation to more complex notions of social justice or collaboration. Evaluation criteria equally evade definition, leaning toward notions of health-promotion. Significantly, the notion of "the person" is readdressed creatively.

CoMT is a site for questioning. It offers a fresh way to express and question foundational mysteries about music therapy, particularly around how we can best understand the way people and music work together. The reluctance of authors to fix and name in terms of predictive approaches and methods is only an advantage, as it challenges us to stay close to the practice and to answer our own questions about the many facets of music therapy. In the next chapters, I will share my own ways of staying close to the practice and consider those facets in more detail.

Toward Formats

The shorthand for all of the above is captured in the notion that "music is incredibly multifaceted" (Stige, 2002, p. 49). The word "facet", pleasingly, has many facets. Originally it refers to one of the small cut and polished faces of a diamond or gem, used figuratively to denote a particular side or aspect of something. In zoology facets are the individual parts or segments of the compound eye of an arthropod, or a small clearly delineated anatomical area. In library science the word refers to each of the several different categories into which something can be simultaneously classified (OED, online).

In all of these meanings, a facet exists only in relation to the larger entity it helps to comprise, whether that is a gem, a library system, or an insect's eye. It can be counted on its own, but its meaning relates beyond itself. Perhaps we can see epistemologies of music in the same way. The neurological foundation of music is important on its own, but its meaning comes to life only when put into relation with, say, the sociological. Perhaps any one way of knowing music is only good in part, at which point it needs to be seen in relation to the other facets of music.

A matrix view acknowledges that the social, the witnessed, and the political have a place amongst those facets. To give music its best chance of being useful, those facets too have to be available, to let in some light, maybe. This, for me, is what CoMT brings. There is an insistence within some CoMT literature that the political and social exists within the material and private. In theory, this can be a challenge to many music therapists. In practice, however, it is liberating, because that works both ways. It means that where you are running a recording session or a band practice, you can also, if needed, attend to the fine motor development involved in adjusting volume levels. If you are assisting in a protest march, you can also be aware of who is unusually singing in time. The matrix of musical experience manifests in multiple ways. The next chapter begins by discussing just one of those more public showings of music therapy work. I hope that it also demonstrates the personal, private, and ongoing practice that led to those showings.

Chapter 4

MATRIX OF FORMATS

Scrap Metal Project

There was a period early in my career when I spent a lot of time in scrap yards and churches. Actually, it was like this: My Friday mornings were spent amongst the recycling bays and metal stores of a scrap yard in a small town in southern England and my afternoons, in the nearby church, hitting reclaimed metal objects with sticks. I was joined by former patients from the local Neurological Rehabilitation Unit, now participants in my CoMT project (Wood, Verney, & Atkinson, 2004). We were doing something that was not only sure and simple, but also new and challenging. Primarily, we were following a music therapy process with aims, structure, and multidisciplinary foundations. At the same time, we were all explorers in an artistic journey. This chapter documents that journey and shares what I learned from it.

From Therapy to Community

Prior to our days in the scrap yard, I had been working as part of a project funded by a UK government body. This project, "From Therapy to Community" (see Atkinson, 2002; Wood, Verney, & Atkinson, 2004) grew from a 15-month pilot to a four-year longitudinal residency in a neurological rehabilitation unit in a small town in southern England. The program followed a three-stage work plan (Fig. 1):

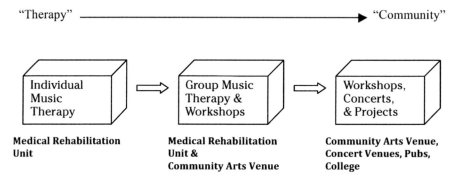

Fig. 1: The three-stage work plan

We had assumed that participants would start the program with individual music therapy, moving to small groups when the time was right, and then transfer on to more independent encounters through workshops in the local arts centre. Here local musicians would be invited to share their own expertise with the program members, facilitated by me as the music therapist. Finally, in stage three, the program members would participate in the community of local music-makers, attending concerts, joining workshops, or attending learning opportunities, supported by my presence or work. Our vision had been that participants could progress at their own pace and that the specific forms of encounter we offered would be bespoke, and supported, according to their interests as well as their needs.

What Is Progress?

There is a tacit understanding within neurological rehabilitation that patients are framed according to a model of recovery. The work of any health professional within that system is focused on the acquisition of skills or insight that can equip the person in their developmental journey from (usually) a traumatic episode back to independent life. There is a similar tacit understanding within the early documented work of Nordoff and Robbins, in which children's work in therapy was framed as a progression from individual to group music therapy and then into the witnessed moments of class performance or musical working games and plays. The process of becoming musical was inherently developmental. "From Therapy to Community" carried this understanding, and whilst avoiding a strict programmatic approach, it was set up with the opportunity of tracking and encouraging progress from dependence to independence.

Typically, this involved a period of up to around 12 weeks of individual music therapy in the hospital or medical environment. Here was familiar music therapy territory. We had rehabilitative goals and a music therapy room with adaptive instruments, and we reported to a multidisciplinary team within the discourse of rehabilitation. Participants acquired physical skills of coordination, grip, stamina, and proprioception. They gained in confidence, insight, and cognitive sequencing. Their simple interactions became more fluent and varied. All of these changes were part of the normal flow of Neurological Rehabilitation and could usually be communicated to colleagues.

For some, this initial period would also involve a spouse or a family member in playing. The skills of functional movement or communication often felt more relevant to them if they were explored within the context of their immediate community and practised together with them. As these skills and relationships emerged, musical interests also manifested. I learned who was a former folk musician and who used to tap dance. Also, what flowed from my own improvisational approach and my background in the idiomatic language of Nordoff Robbins were new musical interests and discoveries. Participants came to be fascinated by musical topics such as minimalism, West African drumming, piano composition, samba, and Gregorian chant. Stage two of the program could offer more in-depth explorations of these areas, facilitated but not always led by me. The final stage of the program enabled participants to create their own communities of interest. They were assisted in attending concerts, joining the local jamming session in the pub, or, in the case of the Scrap Metal Project, devising their own innovative performances.

Progress in music therapy is a multifaceted idea. It's something we look for and encourage, but that is not the only story. The other fundamental stance in music therapy is that we meet a person where they are and that sometimes this is enough. There is a complex relationship between the *aiming* inherent in recovery-based models (working with a named goal) and the *allowing* inherent in musical improvisation or therapy encounters (working without a named goal). Progress is also manifest in different discourses throughout a person's journey. Whilst progress in individual rehabilitative therapy is understood according to goals, skills, and demonstrable physical or communicative ability, in a community arts frame, it might be understood according to the type of social situation tolerated, the pleasure shown in discovering a new style of music, or in being able to attend a session at all.

Equally, not every journey followed the assumed trajectory from individual music therapy to community events. Some took the reverse route or had composite experiences. Rather than only demonstrating "progress", we came also to document a person's "progression". This is a balancing act between the important values of medical rehabilitation and the equally important values of artistic experience.

PJ's Progress

PJ was a tall, slim, and smiling woman in her early 50s. She had found me at a medical rehabilitation conference in the town, where I was running a lunchtime jamming session for attendees. PJ was an attendee at the conference, there as a person with an undiagnosed tremor, possibly out to see what new advances there might be in neurological rehabilitation. Her opening lines to me, as she advanced toward my drum kit, were, *"Can I play? I want to see what I can still do"*.

So here we were, in full view of a circulating conference crowd, attendees milling about with sandwiches and coffee. I was there to offer a little musical fun during the day, along with some information about music therapy. PJ had other ideas: She wanted to learn about herself, to use a new frame of knowing (musical improvisation) in order to make discoveries and diagnoses about her current ability. The effects of her tremor were clear: One arm worked perfectly, the other had a continual and wide-ranging tremor. She had strength in each and a good grip. Her beating was loud, regular, and full of force. What manifested in that moment was a story with two sides: the left, controlled and varied, and the right, more compulsive and monorhythmic. What also manifested was a curiosity to learn more. Clearly, this brief and noisy introduction to music therapy had meant something. We arranged to meet back at the rehabilitation unit the following week.

Thus began six months of weekly individual music therapy sessions. PJ could be part of the "From Therapy to Community" program because she was an outpatient of the service. In the UK, a person can be attached to a medical service without a hospital stay. They are termed "outpatients" and attend appointments periodically. She was physically independent, but her enquiry was so personal, and so related to her psychological adjustment to the onset of her disability, that I suggested we meet on an individual basis. There is an element of security offered by individual music therapy within a medical setting that I could see was important to her. This felt significant especially as she was clearly a reflective person who was sensitive to the signs and situations around her. In CoMT, the semantic messages of a format are part of your strategic choices. Settings (treatment rooms, hospitals), organizational structures (appointments, regular times), and persona (health care professional) matter, literally. They create a level of material reality for the person because a client's expectations and attitude toward the work are created in part by their interaction with these elements. Seeing all these structural elements as part of my wider musical language was integral to choosing the appropriate format.

Within this arrangement, PJ felt confident enough in me, and in the situation, to uncover many facets of her life. Her adjustment to disability was of course painful and awkward, all of which was manifest in our playing. It was also funny and absurd, which also came out. Early sessions were dominated by beating on large drums. Emboldened perhaps by the full, organum accompaniment I often used, PJ quickly trusted both hands to play, and we had music that included intricate rhythmic patterns from one hand and large periodic individual beats from the other. Often these individual beats were aimed at cymbals or gongs, making the most of their resonance and punctuation. An initial rush of joy from this dramatic sound world soon gave way to the pathos and pain of her damaged coordination. This dual rhythmic world was of course a manifestation of a dual functional ability and a psychology that had acquired a duality, too.

Sometimes PJ would play courageously with just the "bad arm", bringing herself into stark confrontation not only with the feeling of her movement but also the sounds of it, redolent with the meaning that these sounds brought. As her accompanist through this time, I underpinned these moments with increasingly dissonant piano figures, marking exactly her beats, softening them sometimes with ostinato passages or harmonic resolutions. PJ's playing often extended into 20-minute periods, without being perseverative or repetitive. It drew out of me a sort of "symphonic" approach to themes, textures, and phrase length. It also warranted the seriousness of intent that comes with large-scale works. Throughout this time, PJ used her voice not to sing, but only in verbal reflection after playing.

Eventually, I came to feel the absence of the singing voice in our music. As an invitation, during one improvisation I sang a low open vowel. To my surprise, PJ imitated it, deep in her own register. From these vocal depths, we began the final stage in our individual journey, rising up together over a number of weeks, both in vocal pitch and also emotionally, through varied scales and modalities, into singing that became light and free. Then, one day, after singing, PJ said, "Becoming disabled can put you on the scrap heap of life. Music makes you beautiful again".

Individuals, Groups, Communities

You may be wondering why this story has appeared in a book about CoMT. After all, CoMT is surely about what is witnessed: the social, the public performance ... not about private, functional, individual therapy. Why do we need CoMT to talk about that?

There is a pragmatic answer to those questions and a theoretical one. Practically, PJ was part of a program in which development of musical activity was integral. She had the option, and the curiosity, from the start to expand her musical horizons over time. So whilst the first format of our activity was individual improvisational music therapy within a clinical environment, we both knew it might not end there. Also, I was working with other participants on a similar basis, and already I was running singing groups or small workshops with those other participants. PJ knew this and was interested in what we were doing. In any case, the thinking involved in identifying needs and interests, then providing the musical context that would meet those needs and enhance those interests, was the same whether I was thinking in the micro (from one chord to another) or the macro (from one workshop course to the next).

The emerging theory of CoMT didn't differentiate between the micro and macro either. It worked on the idea that the private was also already public. Music-centred music therapy deals with what is manifest, what structures are showing themselves in the moment, linking the physical material of a rhythm or tonal movement with the cultural implications of what you are playing, or indeed where. CoMT, deriving as it does for me from that music-centred source, applied just as much to the private phase of my work with PJ as it would to any future public manifestation.

This point of verbal reflection for PJ marked her preparation to join a small group. Soon after, she signalled that she was ready to transfer from individual to small group, joining a group of four other participants. They were verbal, reflective, and creative people. Amongst them was a young man with a traumatic brain injury, two older people who had recently had strokes, a woman with multiple sclerosis, and a carer and a spouse. Early in their meetings, PJ repeated what she had said to me:

"Becoming disabled can put you on the scrap heap of life. Music makes you beautiful again". The others nodded in agreement. They identified with this image, and our conversations started to play with it.

The next week, PJ arrived for the group with a washboard, an old "skiffle" type, pulled from the back of her garage. She also brought some old thimbles from her sewing kit. "Look!" she said, "it makes a noise!" If music could transform her own damaged body into something useful and beautiful, couldn't it surely do the same for these objects? The group laughed, and I started up a folksy tune as she ran the thimbles along the ridges of the washboard. Her "good arm" played whilst the "bad arm" held the board tight. Here was an image of a unified unit, itself embodying the symbol of reclaiming a scrap material and making it beautiful again in music. The others joined in on their percussion, and the washboard was incorporated into the kit.

Week after week, new pieces of scrap were integrated. People brought saucepans, wooden foot massagers, plant pots, fish kettles, and chains. The group would improvise and talk together, and then during the week their creativity would be sparked by spotting something broken or discarded at the back of a cupboard or the dark end of the garden. This act of reclaiming was powerful, because of the symbolic enactment afforded it by their membership of the group.

Soon the conversations turned to what they might want to do next. This group phase had been creative and active, not only through the emergence of this scrap metal symbol, but also through the wide range of musical styles experienced and the solidarity formed amongst the members. Our improvisation had touched on samba, Takemitsu, the experimental works of John Cage, and swing jazz. However, when we came to plan how they might want to expand, away from the hospital setting and out in the community, there was only one place they wanted to go: to the scrap yard.

Facilitating a Project

This project was fortunate to have funds for the apparently absurd and artistic. The only requirements for planning work were that it was safe and professional and that it met the learning standards of the funding body. All the same, here was a stretch: facilitating a project based in a scrap yard, blending the group's clear artistic curiosity with serious rehabilitative and learning goals. What sorts of musical structures would enable that mix to work? What formats would maintain the professional expectations and security, yet keep the process open-ended and really theirs?

I could see by now that the group was confident in improvising together and that playing was a natural mode of communication for them, especially allowing for the range of speech ability amongst the participants. It would be fine for us to meet somewhere safe and just play on old metal objects. But this did not seem to be enough. There would be no real learning goals or symbolic progression in that. This needed a structure that could take their artistic enquiry and situate it in a bigger structure, building and developing something in the process.

Inspired by the experimental approach of John Cage and the large percussion world of samba music, the group came up with the idea of retrieving scrap metal objects from the local recycling centre and then bringing those to the nearby church to be used in musical workshops, alongside their existing orchestral percussion. Our Friday mornings became visits to the scrap yard (set up safely in accordance with our health risk assessments and the manager of the site), which were followed by afternoons of exploration. Sometimes we had sessions where we hit, manipulated, and dismantled objects to find their best sound; other times, we had invited experts in samba, church organ music, or electronic music, in which the group members incorporated the scrap and orchestral percussion in their playing.

My role here was to characterize the developing formats so that they met our needs and interests: to keep them safe, structured, and orientated toward both our creativity and our learning and therapy priorities. Through ongoing reflection with the group and my usual monitoring of our playing, I was able to construct a carefully planned program of workshops. There was no presumption that these would lead to an end-point performance. However, it became clear that the group had performance in mind. Perhaps it started when local churchgoers came into the open space of the church during our workshops. By now our sessions were relaxed, our privacy unprotected. Occasional church visitors would stand and marvel at the sounds we were making. One deliveryman was surprised to have his sack barrow brought into an improvisation, the wheels making a wonderfully intricate rhythmic flare on the stone floor. The spirit of the project had become generous and confident. Whilst I still needed to maintain safety and structure, I also had to acknowledge that this was not a hospital setting and that the group members were now musically active people keen to share their passions.

The Scrap Metal Concert

It is worth wondering why people want to share their music in public. Perhaps the motivation to play music in public is as varied as the people who do it. For the Scrap Metal group members, performance held the prospect of advocacy, particularly of giving a voice to a group of former neurological patients who often fell beneath the radar of public participation. There was also an element of sharing, especially as for many of the group members this had been a process of exciting discovery. They wanted to share that with their friends. PJ reflected on both motivations, also acknowledging a third: personal challenge. The almost pioneering spirit that had characterized her early music therapy had persisted in this community phase. Public performance holds personal challenge for most musicians. It is the moment you discover what you can be, holding within it the promise that you will discover more about yourself. I felt that PJ and others in the group recognized this as an aspect of the project, that the process might be incomplete until they had "gone public" and performed for others what they so loved as a group.

But how to make this work? The development of the project so far had been a mixture of improvisation, absurdity, confrontation of disability and exclusion, composition and learning. We had grown into a trusting group of players who could jam together well and who welcomed onlookers. By now our playing referenced Cage, swing jazz, and stream-of-consciousness poetry. But how would that musical world translate as a concert in this small town in southern England?

My process as a music therapist in this moment was to look at what order, type, and reach of impact were being manifested musically. Our playing was mostly on a core "junk band" of orchestral and scrap instruments. It was metallic, earthy, scruffy, and handmade. This was a musical process rooted in everyday industrial materials; that was where our confidence and identity was. A performance had to reflect that. It also operated on a particular social order that was democratic, flattened by the common experience of disability, and generous in spirit. We had to reflect that, too. The type of impact was personal, nuanced, no longer medical or institutional. It was not commercially driven or tidy. Our performance needed to stay true to the unfussy, straightforward type of musical presence the group had created. It had to feel safe and organized, easy to navigate for those with more complex cognition, but also loose and easy socially. Finally, the reach of the project was local. It had gone beyond the dyadic and the health-based, but it was still rooted in the familiar: family, friends, and local people. The elements for making a safe public performance were already manifest in our weekly sessions; my role here was to honour those elements and let the group members take the next step together.

When the performance day came, we had arrived at a structure that preserved all the elements that felt true to the group. We performed in the church space, by now a familiar venue and sympathetic acoustic. Our instruments were arranged safely but loosely, resembling the scrap yard where they had been found. The concert was a mixture of prepared segments and free improvisation, accompanied by myself on an old stripped-back piano and by two additional music therapists (Mikako Hori and Fraser Simpson) who by now had become indispensable for safety and structure. We warned the audience (a church full of family and friends) that this music might be new to them, that it would be mostly made up on the spot. We told them how we had come to this point, without letting the personae of the group members lapse into their former patient status. And then we played.

In playing, of course, the group members transformed just as much as the scrap metal objects they had salvaged. Just as I saw battered car hoods become huge gathering drums through active use, I also saw former stroke patients become jazz musicians, galvanizing in strength and dexterity. In hearing the parts of an old washing machine ringing like Greek bells, I also saw a person with a traumatic brain injury using more gross motor control than usual. In the same moments, along with those micro changes, I was aware that the place of these musicians in their communities was also changing: Their relationships with family and friends had complexified, and they felt beautiful again.

Formats and Activities

This is not so much a story about the therapeutic power of public performance as about the need to let people and music grow. Growth in music therapy is not only an aspect of the inner world, important as that is. It is material. Development occurs in the order of the physical world, through expansion, accumulation, projection, and incarnation. It also happens through growth in insight, knowledge, and curiosity, in the order of the imagination. Change also happens in a person's social identity, their place in the world, how they are political in the sense of sharing civic space. The question of formats, then, is of how we can think of our own practice in the service of that growth.

Rather than asking how well a new client or patient can meet the demands of your therapy protocol, you could instead ask what therapy protocol will meet the needs and interests of your new client and help them grow. This is how formats emerge. Within the bounds set in your professional culture, and within the safety and ethos of your workplace, the range of ways to help someone grow might be wider than you first thought.

Across the whole "From Therapy to Community" program, I recognized eight main formats for meeting program participants. These had been imagined in broad terms at the start of the project, but not proscribed. In another time and place, the list would be different. It also seemed fair to me that a person involved in a workshop phase should not be treated as if they were having a second-class therapy experience. Every kind of therapy contact should be right for the person, so there was no hierarchy of encounter. To help me think in this way, I developed a model that I called "The Matrix" (Wood, 2006). It was an arrangement of the eight practical formats that were offered during the project, set out in a nonhierarchical order. This was a practical and conceptual response to what I saw as an assumption within music therapy at the time that individual improvisational music therapy was the preferred format in which to do music therapy.

My perception of this assumption in the music therapy profession echoed what Ansdell (2002) termed the "consensus model". This was a heuristic device he used to characterise what he saw as a dominant music therapy approach, based on an individualist psychological model. Ansdell argued that this model prioritised the therapeutic dyad as a primary agent of change, and he contrasted this with the alternative, broader, approach of CoMT. The matrix model did not prioritise this over other formats of music-making, and thus, I felt, created a wider range of possibilities for participants. This in turn generated a wider range of potential participants, activities, places, purposes, and outcomes.

Matrix Diagram of Formats

In 2006, I published my first "matrix of musical formats", setting set out eight formats of music-making in a web of connection. There was no hierarchy or preferred standard method of doing music therapy—just the eight ways of working that in that situation I felt able and compelled to offer. This was the image:

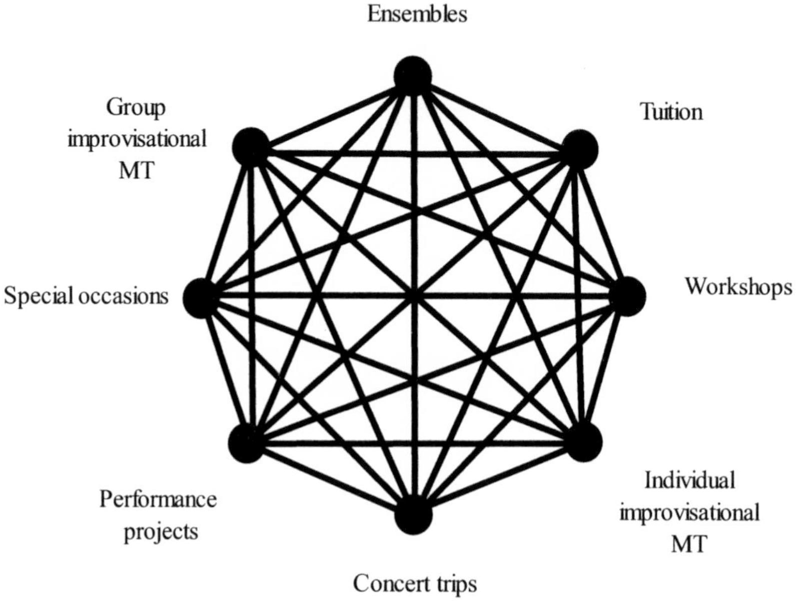

Fig. 2: The matrix of musical formats

The visual elements of this graphic were important in helping me think about what I was offering. The lines of connection reminded me that there was something common in each format of work, the basic musical operation both within us (perhaps viewed neurologically) and amongst us (when seen sociologically) being the material that helps people, whether in a music workshop or individual music therapy. I saw this image as a representation of how music manifests across the orders, types and reach of my practice.

Implications for Theory

Emergence

It is striking how relevant the life of a mass of slime mold is to a music therapist. As I sit in my English office writing this, the woodland several metres away conceals a creature that has become a leading influence in modern science and one that is highly relevant to thinking about music therapy formats. The slimy, gooey substance that coats rotting tree stumps in my nearby woods (slime mold, or *Dictyostelium discoideum*) at first glance looks like one static mass. Observe it over time, and you will discover that it moves imperceptibly across the woodland floor. As the weather conditions change, you might find that the creature has disappeared altogether. Steven Johnson (2001) explains:

> The slime mold spends much of its life as thousands of distinct single-celled units, each moving separately from its other comrades. Under the right conditions, those myriad cells will coalesce again into a single, larger organism. ... When the environment is less hospitable, the slime mold acts as a single organism; when the weather turns cooler and the mold enjoys a large food supply, "it" becomes a "they". The slime mold oscillates between a single creature and a swarm. (p. 13)

This is now recognized as a classic example of "bottom-up" behaviour and shows how a system can be ordered by what Johnson calls "the eerie, invisible hand of self-organization" (p. 16). Self-organization, this quality of groups and swarms that creates order without a leader, generates changes in group behaviour that can be described only in group terms. The rules that describe the behaviour of the individuals cannot be used to describe the behaviour of the whole when seen "from above", and thus new rules "emerge" from the system. The change from basic rules to higher organization is called "emergence", which, along with "self-organization", forms the basis of the theory system known as "complexity theory".

You may not have started this book expecting to ask, "What has slime mold got to do with me?" As a music therapist, I am part of various self-organising, or "complex adaptive" systems. My own body, for example, is a complex adaptive system, as are the work groups I am in, the working relationships, and the cultural contexts in which they are situated. Musical experience itself can be seen as sharing the qualities of a complex adaptive system, both within the body and amongst people, in observable cultural practice and also in terms of function.

A model of music therapy that operates according to a network implies certain qualities in the role and identity of the music therapist and in the relationship between music therapist and client and amongst clients and other connected people. It implies a certain perspective toward all other situational forms or "formats" of music-making and toward their practitioners. It also implies a particular relationship between music therapy and other disciplines. It derives from a different concept of the self, based on a communal model. Finally, it offers a view of music itself as being a world of experience in which organization emerges out of experience and where emergent forms of communal musical organization can be managed as part of the natural flow of music therapy work.

The theoretical basis from related disciplines for developing a concept of emergence is compelling. New musicology, neuromusicology, and music sociology all create models of music and people based on networks and complex systems, whether within the brain, within the mind-body, the whole person, concepts of the self in community or music in everyday life. There is also precedent in music therapy literature, for example, in Pavlicevic's (1997) work on multiple levels of musical structure, which makes use of hierarchical models in her discussion of music therapists' listening. She discusses models from musicology that combine small units of experience with the "bird's-eye view", asking, "When, for instance, do music therapists choose to listen to higher-level structures? When do we listen to the smaller units? What is it that triggers a shift in the hierarchical level that is being focused on?" (p. 82). This use of hierarchy goes some way to reflecting the way musical experience works on different levels, but it does not model the simultaneity in which levels of musical structure are experienced. In a purely hierarchical model, it is difficult to convey the experience of knowing basic or lower-level structure *at the same time* as knowing transcendent or emergent levels.

Second, without a sense of this simultaneity it is difficult to track the progression from one level of musical form to the other in the chronology of a music therapy story. In the example given by Pavlicevic (1997) of Nordoff and Robbins' work with Logan, a triumphant march is seen as the higher-level structure that transcends the "lower-order units" (p. 83). What, then, explains the choice of a song form, the timing of its arrival, the relationship between therapist and client involvement in co-creation? Viewed as a system or "matrix" structure, the resultant song form can be seen as an emergent structure that arises out of the therapists' simultaneous knowing of both the lower levels of structure and the potential for higher-level structure. It reflects the therapist's involvement as integral to the musical matrix itself.

This becomes increasingly important as the scope of music therapy work widens into CoMT programs, where a client may participate in individual music therapy but may progress or simply expand into group and more independent work. This perspective takes hierarchical insights and subjects them to the notion that musical experience is a multifaceted networked experience. Music's multifacity is a reality that music therapy discourse may have resisted addressing, in the interests of "pinning down" practice and technique into treatment models and protocols. The effect of categorisation, or "pinning down", is to create binary distinctions out of complex relations. For example, the line between what we see as "musical" and "paramusical" can be challenged when we categorise or evaluate the process of planning and putting on a concert. Similarly, in music-making, a person is operating both as an individual and as part of context or social structure simultaneously. Consequently, the concept of individual "effectiveness" sometimes is inappropriate when the object of work is to influence social situations, rather than bring about direct cause and effect. The consequence of this thinking about music and people is that our practice carries a technical level of vocabulary that is discretely musical. Does our need to communicate with other professionals dilute our musical thinking?

Working within a set of complex relations like this requires a theoretical framework that can allow those diverse elements to interrelate. Complexity Theory offers a way of playing with multiplicity in a creative and systematic way. As Cilliers writes, the attempt to acknowledge the coexistence of diversity underpins complexity theory:

> "... the argument for a multiplicity of discourses is not a wilful move; it is an acknowledgement of complexity. It allows for the explosion of information and the inevitable contradictions that form part of a truly complex network" (1998, p. 116).

Cilliers describes how components within complex systems form "clusters", connecting to other components in different ways:

> "Although different discourses form "clusters" within this network, they cannot isolate themselves from the network. There are always connections to other discourses ... different clusters in the network may grow, shrink, break up, coalesce, absorb others, or be absorbed." (1998, p. 116)

It is helpful to think of CoMT as a complex system made of musical organization, thinking, and activity, within which related discourses, practices, concepts, and potential can be modelled in interrelation for strategic health purposes. This allows for any element of practice to come into relation with other elements, in the context of them arising out of musical organization, thinking, or activity.

Toward Aims

Practical formats of music therapy sit front and centre in this discussion of complexity and emergence. Although CoMT has become stereotyped as the approach that "includes performance", it is clear from recent accounts in the literature (Curtis, 2015; Stige, et al. 2010) that its scope is wider than just that. It is made of individual stories *that are also* stories about groups and wider social considerations.

All the same, diversity of practice, and the liberty to choose what to do in the interests of clients and settings, is an important signature of this approach. To see all modes of doing music as part of an integrated system helps to keep that liberty coherent and make those choices accountable. An important aspect of thinking about that system is the idea that what we do as music therapists is a manifestation of the client, *plus* you, *plus* the setting—all our connections creating something that cannot be described only by referring to one part. This work needs concepts that describe what emerges from those connections, and that is what matrix thinking is. By allowing those many elements of connection to interact, we can see what is emerging and describe it in concepts that fit. In my view, those concepts tend to be musical, because music itself is an emergent concept, and we have already created a matrix system to work in it.

Yet, we can also look more closely. It is a mystery in musical experience that you can both stand back and also look closely at the same time. It is a stance of attention that many of us recognize, whether naming it fully or not. This stance is possibly more commonly talked about in CoMT because we are presented with choices on both the micro and macro levels more often than with other approaches. CoMT has opened the possibilities of complexity to more choice of activity or public action, but it is still tuned in to the details. Reflexive practice in this approach is not a matter of choosing one or the other, of private or universal, small or big. It is a question of how we integrate both into what we are trying to achieve for people.

In the next chapter, I discuss this through the story of Caryl. Along her extraordinary music therapy journey, I was challenged to think repeatedly about the subject of *aims*. I came to think a lot about how

Caryl changed both in micro physical details and in macro political ways through the same experiences. This in turn made me consider more closely how I should think about our "therapeutic aims". Some things did not happen by direct intervention. In fact, I couldn't really say that anything happened by direct intervention only, and yet here we were identifying need, choosing actions, and making strategies on that basis. Two modes emerge—of *"aiming"* and of *"allowing"*—both seeming to coexist in this approach to practice.

How, in adopting a stance of *"allowing"* in facilitating Caryl's music to manifest fully and without being forced, could I set therapeutic *aims* and account for them? What in CoMT do we aim to do?

Chapter 5

MATRIX OF AIMS

Five Seasons

Of course, part of choosing a format of music therapy is knowing what you want out of it. The question of "why?" is inseparable from "what?" This chapter will focus on music therapy aims, relating that topic to the multiplicity inherent in CoMT. It will also set out some of Deleuze and Guattari's use of the rhizome as a possible model for further theory. We address these through the example of Caryl and the work that culminated in a composition project, Five Seasons.

Caryl was a mature woman living with cerebral palsy in a care home in southern England. We began individual music therapy together in 2003. Although her insight and language were intact, her body was severely limited by the effects of her condition. Spending her days in an adapted wheelchair, Caryl was able to use only her right foot, usually with it resting on a control switch, but sometimes with her leg extended for short periods. Her speech was dysarthric and laboured. She spent six months in individual music therapy. After that time, a new phase of work began in which she wrote poetry, which we set to music together. This phase culminated in a choral song cycle that was performed in a local church by a choir. In enabling this work, I was drawn into continuous reflection on my own approach to music therapy. This new period of rethinking challenged me to justify what value the new work offered Caryl, how to choose our formats and aims within this style of work, and ultimately how it impacted on the wider context.

Early Individual Work

Like PJ's experiences, this "individual story of CoMT" also takes place within a broad program of music therapy. This time, the setting is a care home in southern England. Unlike the Scrap Metal Project, the program here was based almost entirely within the circumstantial community of a large care home. When full, this home had 112 residents. Many were living with a dementia or a chronic neurological condition such as multiple sclerosis. Some had learning difficulties or complex nursing needs. Caryl had lived in her own residence for most of her life, but now required more technical nursing support and physical input due to the advancing limitations imposed by her cerebral palsy.

The music therapy service in the home was funded privately, not charitably; in other words, I was an employee of the home. My approach was to view this large care home as its own village: It had permanent residents, but also a large number of visitors. These visitors were of course staff, but also friends and family of the residents. Within that large community of people, I was relatively free to create modes of doing music therapy that enhanced those relationships and helped elicit or maintain musical skills amongst the residents. The matrix of formats in this setting included individual music therapy, a large singing group, small music therapy groups, walks, quizzes, an opera group, a silent group, musical "hanging out" in social spaces, and joint rehabilitation sessions with physiotherapists and the speech and language therapist.

Because I was visible and present within that community, referrals and requests came from many angles and for many reasons. Whilst I could for myself clarify my main purpose, scope, and boundaries as a music therapist, I could not account for how it was seen and understood by the staff, residents, and visitors around me. Sometimes participants in the program were referred, sometimes they emerged by unplanned social contact, and sometimes they came to find me.

Caryl, like PJ, came to me with this question: *"I want to see what I can still do"*. By now she had already been attending the large singing group and had developed a working relationship both with music and with me. Caryl's mind was determined, curious, and bright. She had in her past been dexterous with her feet, being able to use them to cook, paint, and even knit. Now she could control her motorized wheelchair and a simple environmental switch, but little else. Seeing her physical command diminish, Caryl was keen not to give up too easily. Music therapy for her represented a chance to defy her illness.

Whose Aim Is It?

My aim, too, in any music therapy situation, is to find out what a person can do. I find this a dynamic and inspiring aim. It makes me ask questions of the person through our playing, creating a powerful interaction between what I think of as *allowing* on one hand and *aiming* on the other. In the *allowing,* I recognize that my first purpose is to meet Caryl where she is and to create a nonjudgemental situation where our actions are authentic and trusting. In *aiming,* I recognize that my role is to believe that in music Caryl can discover more and to act on that belief through presenting challenges and new experiences.

In this situation, Caryl's stated aim was to challenge herself and discover new things about herself. What a gift! My notes from that first session say:

> Caryl began playing drum with stick in toes. Able to grip
> + move. I suggested she would be able to play piano at the
> height of her chair, so we tried it—really took to it. Very
> pleasing to her.

> Like ballet! Stretching, pointing, extending ...

The second session notes say this:

> Caryl went straight for piano: this movitation is great ...
> still aiming for clear, precise C major. I have trouble
> knowing what context to use— jazz, A Minor,'romantic',
> etc. Using this falling sequence a lot ...

> ... jazz bass line adds momentum ... swing rhythms just *do*
> bring her in ...

In writing about music therapy, it's very easy to present aims as a *fait accompli.* We sometimes have to articulate them from our own point of view as health professionals. In that frame, I could say that my aims for Caryl were to assess her current state of physical strength, flexibility, control, and range. I wanted to determine her level of musicality: her ability to co-create in improvisation and to use music communicatively and expressively. All these would be valid ways of justifying my therapeutic choices in the early sessions. They would be true.

However, another set of aims is present. Caryl herself wants to know how she can move. Maybe she wants to feel her body exercising, exerting power and control over an object, to have the satisfaction of impacting upon the world and of creating something out of nothing. Perhaps she wants fun, a meaningful and pleasurable moment with someone. I would wish these for her, too. In her verbal feedback, Caryl gave some clues about what was valuable to her personally:

> It's brill, because I've always wanted to play the piano ... I never thought I would play it. I'm losing the feeling in my foot so I can't do anything—but it doesn't matter with this. I go by hearing my music.

Within this moment for Caryl, new aims do emerge out of the experience of hearing her music. These are the achievement of a personal ambition, defiance of disability, and pleasure.

But the question of aims does not end there. I have mine, Caryl has hers. But a third set emerges in this matrix of purpose. The music we start to make has its own inner demands. During our playing, more concrete, detailed aims arrive. Session 4 notes say, "... singing: raising tone slowly—working very hard to maintain tone and enunciate". In moments such as this, what matters is the production of a tone and a consonant. We both know why this matters from our own points of view, but right now it matters for its own emergent sake: *maintain tone and enunciate.*

It also matters that the word being sung in this moment is *Don't.* It is repeated twice more: *Don't. Don't. Don't*—I wait—*patronize me.* She is singing to the world outside. *Don't. Don't. Don't ... ignore me.* She completes the phrase: *Just listen. Listen. Listen! ... to me.* What is my aim now? To show unequivocally that I am listening. I do this not by imitating but by joining, underpinning at the piano, playing as closely as possible with the unfolding narrative. The harmony is minor, coloured with augmented fourths and minor seconds. Its rhythm is abrupt and accented, like the singing. Now our aims converge: to maintain the line and arrive at the end of the phrase, so that we can discover what it is. What word, what chord, what timing?

Often in music-centred music therapy we talk about "what the music wants". There is a tendency to anthropomorphize music, asking "Where does it lead?" or "What does it need?" This is a necessary shorthand, but only amongst people who have a common understanding about where this tendency comes from. More technically, we might think of this question in terms of emergent aims. In the moment of playing, what emerges between Caryl and myself, out of the combined forces of our abilities, desires, and interests, is something that can be known only musically. The joint aim emerges as *maintain tone and enunciate.* It is something that can be described only using musical terms, like phrasing, timing, and rhythm. What we often do outside of that is to put this emergent aim back into our own form of vocabulary for the purposes of evaluation.

In her early individual music therapy sessions, Caryl covered a lot of ground. She played percussion instruments with adapted sticks attached to her right foot and with thimbles on her toes, sang well-known songs wrote lines of poetry to improvise vocally, and invented vocal exercises with me for daily use. I monitored her progress and carried out evaluations of this practice using the Nordoff Robbins rating scales (Nordoff & Robbins, 1977, pp. 177–208; 2007, pp. 372–418). During the period of work with Caryl, I did not use the third Nordoff Robbins scale, "musicing", which was published in the 2007 edition of *Creative Music Therapy*. The first two scales divide musical experience into two developmental scales— of "communicativeness" and "coactivity". Within these two scales, the dimensions in which the client changes are described in reference to a concept of musical experience, described through observation of musical behaviour. In this phase of individual music therapy, the purpose of evaluation was to track Caryl's own progress, observed during her times playing music with me in the workroom, and chart that progress against the aims, techniques, and strategies that were being used.

New Aims

When Caryl told me that she had started to write poems that she wanted set to music, I noted that we were entering a new phase of music therapy work. Spurred on by her early improvisations, Caryl told me that she now spent her evenings thinking of full poems and memorizing them. During her music therapy sessions, she would recite the poems and I would transcribe them. We would then improvise, transcribe, and discuss melodies to go with the poems. I observed that aspects of Caryl's musical life were proliferating. During this time, I was aware that Caryl's musical activity was no longer confined to the workroom or to her time with me. This involved her singing solos in the care home's choir, expanding her vocal exercises every morning with her carer, and taking more interest in musical history through her recreational listening. She was living more fully as a musical person throughout her life.

It seemed natural within the terms of my workplace program that

I should support this musical expansion. My contact time with Caryl was limited, yet her musical and developmental ambitions were not. How should I choose the formats or activities that would help Caryl, and within those, how could I set therapeutic aims? There were things I had already perceived about Caryl's progress. She worked best in 1:1 situations, owing to her limited mobility, field of vision, and vocal power. She was verbally reflective, culturally attuned, and socially isolated. She was also developing functionally and motivated by this new use of her body.

Her progress was helped by individual encounters, oriented toward both her interactions and her physical ability. Much music therapy theory, including CoMT, combines those two aspects implicitly. For certain decisions I felt it was important to be able to separate them into categories. This work was active in two ways: functionally (in relation to how Caryl's body works) and interactively (in relation to how she could use that functionality for social or cultural purposes). Knowing that really the two worked together, like yin and yang, my reflective processes had to work in the material realities of care provision and care reporting. The music therapy formats had to reflect this. We had to offer mostly 1:1 encounters, structured to derive both functional and interactive benefit, taking into account a wider cultural connection and an ongoing musical practice. This thinking led to a program that included:

- Weekly 1:1 session of 30 mins. This was improvisational in approach, but often included work on poetry, singing known songs or listening to music.
- Daily vocal exercises with keyworker during personal care times. This was facilitated by a specially recorded CD that I had produced based on Caryl's Speech and Language needs.
- Intermittent joint sessions with Speech and Language Therapy.
- Participation in care home's weekly singing group.

These activities of course generate a range of processes, aims and outcomes. They vary between highly structured functional elements such as a CD of vocal exercises for repetition and times of reflective unplanned discovery in musical improvisation. Some aims could be tracked in clear observable terms, such as diction or breath control. Others, such as social involvement, less so. One aspect that emerged unexpectedly, becoming particularly interesting to track, was a composition project that came to be called "Five Seasons".

Projects Emerge from Practice

The process of "Five Seasons" was emergent in a number of specific ways. First, it surprised us both when an improvisation around one of Caryl's poems turned into a clear duet structure. I realized that Caryl was able to imagine more than one voice in her music. She was not only participating in social musical work but also imagining and creating it, too. This was emergent in the sense that we discovered it together. Within her singing, there was of course not only a focus on the functionality of her diction and breathing, but also an awareness of the content in her lyrics and what that meant in her interactions with a listener. She had something to say, and one aim was to process and present that meaning well. This was emergent in the sense that we enacted both elements in the same unitary moment of singing. When she later asked for her work to be sung by a choir, it also became clear that Caryl had a vision about performance. Whilst she was not interested in performing personally, she was, however, keen to have her songs sung by others. Through this emergent compositional work, Caryl would be able to in some senses emerge physically from the care home into a local community of listeners.

I had observed that Caryl wrote about what she saw from her window. She loved nature, especially the birds who visited her feeders and the trees that changed with the seasons. We had reflected on this interest in the outside world, particularly on how the long-term writing process lends itself to accounts of the changing seasons. Caryl loved this idea. When we came to name the final work, which was by now a song cycle of six pieces for women's choir, we reflected on the big themes. The main focus for Caryl was the solace that nature gives her. She had written this refrain for one song:

leaves grow
leaves turn
leaves fall
and they grow again

In a poetic moment together, we noted how the cycle of nature is not limited to just four seasons, because the final moment of winter is already the beginning of spring. It felt more natural to talk of five seasons, pointing to the promise of rebirth within the darkness of winter. During these free-flowing reflections, my aims as a music therapist were layered. There were micro details, around keeping our exchanges short, mixing closed and open questions, and giving Caryl the optimum chance to practice her speech and get her meaning across. In that moment, I was also aiming to elicit and synthesise the meaning of our conversation and to put that in context for her. At the same time, we were working toward a goal, which was to create and produce a choral work for performance. Sometimes the aim was beyond us, toward a finished product. Again, the bigger emergent aim was to facilitate for Caryl an optimum musical experience that really met her needs (functional and interactive) and enhanced her potential.

Caryl's first song cycle, "Five Seasons", was eventually performed in her local church, by a choir. Caryl was at the performance, which was filmed. By now, Caryl was not the only person benefiting from the music therapy practices that had developed around her, as this event included a choir and an audience, all of whom were contributing participants in the change that music was bringing. I could also see that senior members of her care home company who heard the concert were inspired and felt that something had been changed in their relationship to Caryl, to music, to the local community, and to their own work. Months and years later, people viewing the film continued to be moved and inspired by Caryl's music.

In practical terms, Caryl was participating in more formats than she had previously, which meant that our aims had diversified. Sometimes she improvised or rehearsed music with me on her own in the workroom. These contrasting modes of music-making already signified that Caryl was sometimes working toward an agreed end point (when rehearsing), but at others had no clearly stated musical aim (when improvising). At other times, she was the author of a musical work that was being rehearsed by a choir during the week. At times, I was responsible for a specific, improvisational music therapy session, in which anything could happen out of our interactions. Elsewhere, yet still within the context of this work, I was pursuing a strict agenda over weeks or months: making a performance happen, in rehearsals with the choir or in conversation with the concert organisers. These different formats of work, and varying aims, diversified significantly during this phase of work.

New Context, New Evaluation

The formats of practice had diversified, and thus the context in which I now worked with Caryl had widened. It was now more visibly a cultural milieu within which Caryl was contributing, rather than only a limited health care setting in which she was receiving therapy. Within this milieu, the impact of her music therapy work was not always directly observable. Senior directors from her care home company wrote after the concert that their ideas about care had been enriched by the event. They told other colleagues about what they had seen, using their own notions of why it had value to them. Those notions of value included value to staff morale, value as an example of good care practice, and value for public relations. We were in a new context of values, not only of people or of place.

This widespread communication about the value of Caryl's music therapy work showed me a potential impact within the company that I was unable to monitor using traditional, individual-based approaches. It was not my professional purpose as a therapist to improve staff morale, model good care practice, or help with PR. Yet I could see these were valuable beneficial outcomes. The visibility of the work and its stated aims of representing Caryl to a wider community contributed to the prominence of these beneficial outcomes within the work. I at least had to communicate about them, along with the individual aims and outcomes for Caryl that everyone agreed were the point of the work. I was increasingly challenged by the communication methods available when reporting to people more widely. Methods such as corridor chats, detailed music therapy analysis, and daily catch-up meetings were viable reporting methods only when the scope of my evaluation was circumstantially in one care setting. To communicate the personal meaning of Caryl's work to a widespread and varied range of people in the company was a new challenge.

This set of circumstances created a new professional dilemma for me. To give full consideration to evaluating this work, I had to articulate the value inherent in the impact of the concert on the cultural life of the town, on the complex organizational structures of the care home company, and in the changing practical experiences of Caryl's life. It seemed misrepresentative of Caryl's own process for me to isolate her as only the recipient of therapeutic benefit. I also felt it was important to recognise that in enabling this public performance, I had become a collaborating partner with Caryl on a social and cultural level.

My own professional responsibilities and expectations were changing. My first response to this change was to expand my use of the Nordoff Robbins rating scales for application in this case, adding higher levels of participation within the "communicativeness" and "coactivity" scales. This expansion allowed me to include elements of project participation and cultural contribution (Wood, 2006). This expansion of the rating scales still raised questions for me about evaluating this broader approach to music therapy, as I was changing the appearance of evaluation tools without engaging thoroughly with the theoretical implications of a change to the approach.

One Size Fits All?

I discovered through my own doctoral research that I wasn't alone in finding a poor fit between the breadth of what I did and the narrow scope of the mechanisms that were available to think about it. This goes to the heart of choosing formats and setting aims, because even if you feel a theoretical liberty and have institutional backing to broaden your practice, you will also feel rightly accountable to your profession and discipline to know what you are doing and why. These are important knowledge practices. And if you are in that position, you are certainly not alone.

When I started the preliminary study for my doctoral project, I wondered if other people felt the same as me. I learned through interviewing other music therapists working broadly in UK care homes that many practitioners who have liberty to act broadly have misgivings about how they choose, monitor, and communicate about those actions. Through my interviews and analysis, I came to five insights about the fit between practice and the stages of forming knowledge around it. They were:

Insight 1	Practical activities of evaluating, planning, and communicating everyday music therapy practice are diverse and flexible and seek to optimise the experience of the user.
Insight 2	Conceptual tools for such evaluating, planning, and communicating are diverse and flexible and seek to optimise the experience of the user.
Insight 3	Evaluation has a direct connection with professional identity.
Insight 4	The workplace shapes practice; it places limits and necessitates further staff awareness of music therapy.
Insight 5	Reflexivity is complex, in that it occurs in multiple time frames, involving multiple levels of information, including material circumstances, prevailing ethos, individual and communal timing, music therapy purpose, and political impact.

Fig. 3: Five insights on evaluation

These insights showed me some of the dilemmas around choosing formats, setting aims, and communicating outcomes in the context of everyday health care settings. They also helped explain in my own mind why some of those dilemmas exist. I hope that in sharing them here, I may offer some comfort to others who have felt the same way. It also sets a wider reflective scene for how I share my own methods of thinking.

Practical Activities of Evaluation

I learned that music therapists use a wide range of practical activities in their music therapy thinking. My first insight was that:

- Practical activities of evaluating, planning, and communicating everyday music therapy practice are diverse and flexible and seek to optimise the experience of the user.

Diverse Activities

It was striking how many activities of evaluating, planning, and communicating practice came through in my interviews with the music therapists, even within a limited number, in a limited range of care homes, and without my seeking to create a compendium of methods. The list of activities included indexed recordings, written session notes, musical notation, own-devised charts, box-ticking forms, verbal descriptions and categories, by memory recall, comparing the client inside music to how they are outside, observing body movements and gesture, from client feedback, using practitioners' own terminology and concepts, thinking about musical preferences, thinking about group experience and individual, how much a client knows about music, by looking at the instruments used, with reference to music history, and by writing assessment logs. This suggested not only that there are many ways of carrying out professional thinking, but also that our thinking adapts according to purpose or timing.

Link Between Evaluation and Planning

My contact with other music therapists helped me question the link between what we plan to do and how we then judge its success. This link also was diverse, showing how flexible in practice music therapists are required to be. One described how feedback from staff or families was a key feature in her planning:

> MT   the staff and the relatives will say, "oh my goodness,
> so and so has come back from this group … and he
> hasn't looked like this before" or "normally he's in his
> room with very low spirit", so you know people are
> commenting because it's not shut away …

Others, by contrast, stated that they worked from more formal evaluations:

> MT   … a summary of what happened, it might include the
> time of day it was at, in case I want to look back at
> that, it might include a little manuscript of a key
> theme or something I was working on, or just a mode
> I might have been using … that's where I keep my
> notes for the next week, and it's also where I start off
> the next week, just looking over them before the day
> starts …

CoMT often creates flexible stages of work, from individual to group, requiring practitioners also to consider time-tabling that is both planned and unplanned. Apart from the physical requirements of how to position instruments, for example, other forces are also present in our choices—for instance, the questions of functional goals, social goals, or emotional change, as seen in this example:

> SW   you know, because music happens on so many levels
> in a person and in a situation, you put it in a situation
> and see which one flowers. And sometimes it can be
> confusing because it flowers in more than one
> direction at the same time … in that situation, already
> there's a social flowering, but it might also be an
> emotional one, for someone else, and a functional
> one for someone …
> MT   … yes, you've hit the nail on the head …

I learned that in CoMT, we often have to be highly adaptive and innovative in linking our choices to the many knowledge activities we perform. This link can be seen in the variety of structural elements with which we work, such as individual and group times, "loose time", changing session times, and integrating with the home itself. It is also demonstrated in the more tacit processes of simultaneous decision-making, relating information from previous experience to information from formal assessments and immediate experience in a singular moment. This is described below as occurring in a context where practitioners are operating also on the level of empathy, possibly between private and public worlds, and, crucially, on the level of potential:

> MT   Well, I don't just observe it, I think all these things as
>   I'm doing it.

The relationship between evaluation and planning, on a practical level, is that the music therapist's music in the moment is actually the tip of a highly specialist iceberg.

Another problematic, often-hidden dimension to the practice of planning and evaluating is that it can sometimes be on the basis of hazy, piecemeal, or tentative thought, as demonstrated in this brief quote:

> MT   ... if I'm completely honest, when I'm in there I'm
>   not thinking ...

This may also signify a lack of regard for the types of thinking that characterize music therapy reflectivity. Whilst music therapists sometimes don't knowingly engage in formal analytical or procedural thought, we are always making highly specialised and integrated observations, responses, and connections in the moment.

Problem of Communicating

One common dilemma for practitioners doing broad-based work in community settings is that whilst they are confident of their own personal convictions and beliefs and of the content of their training, few have strong and ready-made concepts for describing or justifying every part of their work. It is common for them to find difficulty in verbalising not only the innovations in their practice, but also the complexity of it:

> MT   I suppose that's singing something that we know, or
>   making some music that we know, and maybe doing

> it in a way which is more conventional ...
>
> SW   Conventional to who?
>
> MT   Well, exactly, what do I mean by conventional? Every
>   time I open my mouth to say something, I'm
>   analysing what I'm saying ...

This may point to a lack of satisfactory discourse within CoMT around aims and evaluation, but it may also indicate that the mode of interdisciplinary communication varies widely in practice. Care plans, mixtures of formal and informal verbal feedback, brief personal notes, and attending formal meetings predominate as methods by which we actively communicate our work. Equally, however, practitioners in CoMT are viewed in practice and therefore have to "model" their approach and their attention to other staff:

> MT   there's one sister who keeps an eye on everything, and
>   she's really interested in what's going on, so if there's
>   something particular that sits in my mind as being
>   something that needs to be communicated verbally,
>   she'd be the person that I'd see.

The problem of language emerges in this insight, too, showing music therapists to struggle when it came to verbalising their ideas and their practice:

> SW   Is it easy to communicate the content of what you've
>   done?
>
> MT   It always sounds so rubbish when you say it back ...
>   it really does! It's like, "oh, you really had to be there"
>   ... it's really hard to put it into words.
>
> SW   OK, why?
>
> MT   Uh ... because I think ... well, it's that whole thing
>   of the nature of music. As soon as you put it into
>   words, something is lost.

I was given the impression that the move from choosing aims to creating formats, planning action, enacting it, and then communicating it entails a transformation of knowledge. What feels like a natural process for the music therapist is actually a complex, constructed technology, in which information is processed through reflective moments of observation, assessment in the light of previous knowledge, application in the light of circumstances, and then assessment in the new moment. Then, in retrospect, a further set of appraisals occurs in reflection. The problem here is one of translation: the act of making things that are different somehow equivalent.

Focus of Evaluation

Sometimes, the value of work in CoMT is in part how it has represented one group (say, people living with dementia) to another group (say, carers). Where the locus of therapeutic attention is often the client *plus* the workplace, it follows that the locus of our thinking may also be the workplace or the systems that support it. We may sometimes therefore have to consider aims that can link client or group experience with consequent workplace or contextual change. We then have to ask how cause and effect (in terms of music therapy interactions) can be linked with political or social impact. Would this stop at the close locality of a therapy setting, or could it be relevant on an organizational or community level? In other words, does CoMT raise a fundamental question about the nature of 'the client'? If so, how do we build that into our aims?

Aims and Timing

One of my favourite musical mantras is "Timing is everything". This is especially the case in community settings, where a person might vary widely in response according to the time of day or the mood of a place. It is common that music therapists consider the element of timing in relation to their planning, actions, and communications. This is largely within a wider approach of optimising the impact of the experience for the client, for themselves, and for the workplace—for example, in this extract:

> MT I kind of see it as part of my role, to catch those times, to engage with people when they show a desire to, because they might not …

and also in this example:

> MT … I always see one particular resident before lunch

> because she has her lunch in the music therapy room
> with her husband …

The adaptation of practice according to clients' optimum responses suggests that our aims and expectations may also change according to timing.

Conceptual Tools

My second insight concerned the conceptual tools we have available for choosing, planning, and communicating CoMT. It states:

> Conceptual tools for such evaluating, planning, and communicating are diverse and flexible and seek to optimize the experience of the user.

Diverse Conceptual Tools

The conceptual tools that accompany, and in some cases form, the practical methods of CoMT practice are equally diverse and flexible. In my research interviews, they included notions of timing, subtle degrees of change in approach toward clients according to mood or circumstance, conceptualising how music therapists fit in the workplace setting and how music therapy fits, creating context-specific categories for evaluation according to individual resident needs, and thinking on different levels at the same time.

Source of Conceptual Tools

Some of these tools appear to be derived from music therapy training, particularly, perhaps, when considering the categorising of experience into elements such as "emotional", "physical", "memory", or "coordination", etc. It is symptomatic of CoMT that each practitioner may have differing sets of criteria or at least a divergent sense of priority within them. Similarly, the skill of thinking in complex organization, incorporating split-second musical decisions, background knowledge about residents, and personal foundational beliefs, may be acquired on a training and developed thereafter to a lesser or greater extent by experience:

> SW   Does that come under your understanding of these

> people's needs, the residents' needs, one of them
> being freedom of movement?
>
> MT Yes, and also the difficulty of getting them to settle,
> to do something together, you know, a sort of
> community experience, and doing something which
> they enjoy and something which will evoke memories
> and give them something to talk about maybe, and
> give them some sort of common ground for a social
> activity ...

Our actions depend on our understanding of need in a situation, but it is
not always easy to translate our understanding of need into action and
beyond into a professional language.

Multiple Time Frames

One aspect of this, perhaps, is the problem of time frames. Almost all
music therapists think in multiple time frames. That is, whilst planning or
playing in the present, we make judgements on the basis of prior
knowledge, memory recall, present interaction, and what *may happen*. We
link our *allowing* in the present to *aims* from the past and those for the
future. This awareness of potential, the "imaginary" or the possible, is
another characteristic element in the process of choosing formats and
setting aims. This element in itself creates a challenge to the standard
structures of professional communication. Perhaps a discipline that works
with a creative art form requires a concept of potential at its core?

Planning and Goals

The problem with planning and communicating on the basis of what "may
happen" is that the music therapist can appear haphazard and, more
important, risks failing to meet functional goals. Where written planning
can "set things in stone", music therapists find themselves limited to
achieving someone else's aims, meeting an end point predicted by others
or in another time, rather than progressing to an end as yet unknowable:

> SW So you could find yourself in a situation where a
> formally referred regular client, using that
> terminology, was not responding, therefore music

> therapy wasn't working, and someone who pops in,
> has ten minutes of very strong engagement
> informally, but maybe not in the classic music therapy
> sense of the word, is working … has that ever
> happened, have you ever had a day when you think
> "my regulars feel like it's a failure" but those "party
> moments" were great? … has that ever happened?

MT   Sure, yeah …

This appears to be more than a problem of language or a question of functional goals. It seems to be a paradox of music therapy practice, brought much more clearly to light by CoMT than arguably any other approach. At the point of planning practice on the basis of formulated aims, music therapists themselves need conceptual tools that accommodate multiplicity, allowing functional development where it occurs and making good use of it in evidence where possible.

Witnessed Practice

A main element in this paradox is that in CoMT, a significant amount of our practice can be witnessed by other people, such as families and staff. This has direct consequences for those people's use of space, time, and resources. This act of witness may affect the setting's mood, its public relations, or the music therapist's professional standing within the structures—either positively or negatively. It is important that music therapists know the expectations and needs of the setting. It is also important that they are not fettered by those expectations.

Another dimension of this particular paradox is the problematic use of the term "performance", particularly in CoMT literature. Whilst this has proved a useful tool for articulating the notion of "becoming" in music and in situating public displays of music-making within a more dispassionate and connected music therapy language, it has had the effect of stereotyping the approach as a strand of practice concerned solely with performing works in front of others. Arguably, it has had the opposite result to what was intended.

Professional Identity

My third insight concerned how we evaluate practice in relation to aims within the music therapy profession. It states:

- Evaluation has a direct connection with professional identity.

Professional Duty

The way music therapists described evaluating their practice showed that they were strikingly concerned with their professional identity. In its basic sense, evaluation was seen as a professional duty and, in that way, taken for granted. It may be problematic in CoMT, due to the tension between this professional duty and the sense that we may lack the proper conceptual and practical tools to fulfil that duty formally.

> MT   I guess it's the formality, but then music therapy isn't always formal … I guess it's just a label …
>
> SW   What's inside the label for you?
>
> MT   Uh … boundaries, for sure …
>
> SW   By which you mean …?
>
> MT   I'm saying this and I know my own boundaries are different, but a weekly or a regular intervention at a regular time, but also … a boundary of … taking notes in a particular way. As soon as it become music therapy, I feel almost duty-bound to treat it … and it's not a case of better or worse, but I'm clinically thinking differently. As opposed to when it's just a musical interaction, it's still in so many ways music therapy, but how I feel duty-bound to treat it is maybe different …

This implies that whilst music therapists in CoMT can show they evaluate their work in diverse ways and at different times, they don't feel they can evidence this effectively or differentiate between "types" of musical interaction. Consequently, they often devise their own methods of describing what they do and why it is of value, or they move between the functional and the interactive in focus. A discomfort amongst the music therapists in this regard possibly demonstrates the awkwardness, unknowingly, of occupying quite different territories of knowledge at the same time (the functional and the qualitative, for example, or the formal and informal).

Professional Expectations

My conversations with music therapists also showed how they were affected by the circumstances and expectations of the workplace. This burden can be felt personally, perhaps, but also, from this data, purely as a professional: the concern that in making music therapy choices and communications, practitioners are representing their profession and either nurturing their standing as a professional or somehow damaging it. At the same time, in accommodating the breadth of workplace expectation, music therapists risk trying to serve and satisfy too many competing agendas. There could be a danger of being overburdened by responding to the complex system of expectations and interests in the workplace.

The Workplace Shapes Practice

The fourth insight showed the impact of the workplace on CoMT practice. It states:

- The workplace shapes practice; it places limits and necessitates further staff awareness of music therapy.

Responding to Context

Context can challenge music therapists both in terms of how they choose their formats and aims and in how they frame their practice and what it might mean:

> MT   When I first went in … I had this model and that was where I felt safe, that was where my work had been. I just wanted a little room that was safe to work in, that was private, with all my things around me, but I very quickly learned that that was not going to work
> …
>
> … I think it was a feeling of having practised music therapy in a certain sort of a way, not so much the practice of the music therapy but the environment, the physical environment in which you practised it, it had got to be so much a part of my culture, that this

> was where music therapy takes place, in a room with
> four walls with the the door shut, and nobody … and
> I think it was because I'd done that for such a long
> time, it was quite difficult to feel that actually it could
> be practised in a different environment. My heart told
> me one thing and my head told me the other, that
> actually it was fine …

Whereas the traditional assumption about music therapy might have been that a pure form of interaction existed somehow beyond the physical limits of buildings or jobs, the experience of practitioners in CoMT is that the workplace is of direct influence in shaping their work. Rather than indicating a lack of clinical direction or focus, the approaches discussed above show courage and integrity in going beyond the long-standing or newly acquired habits of professional practice in order to make meaningful meeting happen in that context. As another example, some music therapists report how their work has to be informal because of the shape or use of their building.

Collaborative Practice

The corollary of working along with the setting in this way is that a much more direct collaboration with carers or other staff is necessitated. This understanding can come from difficult experiences where a lack of communication creates unease or mistrust. In other situations, the need for collaboration comes from a clearer, purpose-driven approach.

Increased Number of Participants

It is also characteristic of CoMT that the impact of the work might reach a relationship of which the music therapist is not directly a part. In some instances, the role of the music therapist is to introduce others to musical communication and enable them to take it for themselves into their ongoing lives. In that situation, the focus of the aims and formats may be not only the resident, but also the carer, family member, staff member, or institution.

Reflexivity Is Complex

In my fifth insight, I touched on the multiplicity inherent in practice. I learned:

• Reflexivity is complex, in that it occurs in multiple time frames, involving multiple levels of information, including material circumstances, prevailing ethos, individual and communal timing, music therapy purpose, and political impact.

Intimations of Multiplicity

The often unacknowledged stance for writers in CoMT is that multiplicity refers not only to the order, types, and reach of practice or to the probable breadth of formats and aims within it, but also, used technically, to the emergent properties of the system as a whole. This system involves practice, theory, time, and organizational forces. One example of this is the notion that the witnessing of CoMT by others may impact upon your choices, aims, and actions. Questions regarding how music therapy is understood and valued by onlookers, how it contributes to a setting's atmosphere, and how it makes staff feel may all be active considerations in your planning and also potentially in the manner, content, or impact of your reporting.

Capturing Multiplicity: Functional Interaction

CoMT sets a wide scope for how it frames the task of enhancing a person's musical life. The challenge is to capture the multiple in a simple phrase. I understand multiplicity as allowing for impact both on the individual functional level and on the sociocultural level of interaction. This is supported by a belief that music is an emergent property of function and interaction in operation together. A person can be known best in musical terms because musical terms are already a combination of what is happening (the function) and what this is in relation to (the interaction).

A good example of this can be found in the brief notes a music therapist has to write in care records. Music therapists often despair when the fullness of a person's music therapy session has to be summarized into a sentence for a care plan or medical note. When the wholeness of life that we touch in a vocal improvisation is reduced to a phrase like "She sang", we squirm at how little of our work can be represented in words. *She sang* gives us two lines of thought. First, we point to a realm of functional ability: There was breath, coordination, tone, projection, movement, and articulation. Next, we also point to a realm of interaction: There was a listener, a motive, a style, a context, or a cultural form. *She sang* says both, although it feels like it says neither. My aims in relation to that emerge in the hybrid term of functional interaction.

What in practice is meant by functional interaction? CoMT can often be assumed wrongly to focus only on performance, pleasure, or distraction. Whilst these are all aspects of practice that can have strategic benefit in music therapy, they make up a small part of the whole. Aims in this approach can be linked equally with the promotion of functional skill, manifest in co-creative, purposeful, interaction. The methodology for this approach essentially understands a person's music to emerge out of the joint operations of functional skill and social interaction. Their musical profile can then be described in terms of how their functional skills work together for the purposes and in the context of interaction. Inferences regarding well-being or quality of life can then be made on the basis of the person's composite functional interaction. In practice, this means that a person with low functional skill may not necessarily have low well-being, if their opportunities to use those skills interactively are maintained. Equally, a person with higher skill levels may be assumed to have high quality of life, yet this may be a false inference unless their skills are used interactively.

Dimensions

One of the threads in this book is to share some initial thoughts on how we can work with functional interaction on paper. In this chapter, I explore how to think about aims and formats through a matrix of ten dimensions of experience. This set of dimensions resonates with other models of assessment and evaluation (e.g., Baxter, et al., 2007; Carpente, 2013) and provides an overview of what a person can do and how they use it interactively. These dimensions act as a frame to focus me on how the person is active musically across a fixed set of skills. The dimensions are:

- Fine Motor
- Gross Motor
- Oral Motor
- Sensory
- Attention
- Expression
- Social
- Emotional
- Cognitive
- Creative

These dimensions reflect a wide range of experience within the person when active musically. The person's musicality is understood not as one dimension amongst these but instead by observing the interplay and organization amongst these elements. This range of dimensions has been derived from consultation amongst music therapists working in care homes. The dimensions active in music are not limited by the social context in which the music therapy is occurring. That is, a person in individual music therapy will still demonstrate social skills; a person in structured rehabilitation therapy can still work toward increasing creativity and expressiveness; and a person in a community performance project could benefit in terms of fine motor development and personal expression. The profile of the person's musicality within these situations will be illustrated by how these ten dimensions reconfigure over the course of their session. There is further discussion of these and their application in a full assessment methodology in Chapter Seven.

Politics of Aims

Individual dimensions? Skills? Aims? These are the remit of CoMT? I would argue that they are, for a number of reasons. CoMT theory has never suggested that individual transformation doesn't matter. In fact, almost all CoMT reporting has been in the form of individual case study. What has differed is the inclusion of the wider context into either the choice of music therapy format or the theoretical interpretation of the process.

That interpretation has explored alternatives to the pure individualism of reductive objectivist science. It draws on a broader or more flexible concept of the person, a more socially based understanding of health, and the intersubjectivity inherent in performativity. With that, music therapy practice has thus been opened up to the possibility of impacting on more than only the skill level of an individual, through more than only individual music therapy session formats. Where music therapists have worked with people in a more complex way, as with Curtis (2011, 2012) and Oddy (2005), for example, CoMT has tended to provide a rationale or justification for the style of work, but not a satisfactory approach to reporting and evaluating it.

This is not because authors and practitioners in CoMT are unable to provide this thinking, but more commonly because the reductive processes necessary to report widely have felt counterintuitive. There is a bad fit between the spirit and approach of some CoMT work and the spirit and approach of the commonly accepted credible reporting mechanisms within our health, education, and social care sectors.

Matrix Flowchart of Aims

The choice of formats and setting of aims is a political as well as personal business. We acknowledge in CoMT that our practice exists within a complex system of agendas, variable practices, interests, and needs. It is impossible to account for this complex system of possibilities in a practical diagram, but it is possible to ask sensible, helpful questions. The matrix of aims in my approach to CoMT is not so much a diagram as a flowchart. It is a way of eliciting thinking that guides action.

There is always a wonderful creative leap between fixing a category on paper (such as deciding a person has "moderate fine motor control") and then making choices on whether to seek to enhance that skill, in what format, and to what end. Still further, when we come to playing music, our creative leaps become even less traceable. I believe there is a tacit understanding in CoMT that the categories and creative leaps inherent in thinking about this approach can apply to any person in any format of music. In other words, taken as a whole, a person is active across the same dimensions of being whether they are minimally responsive in 1:1 neuro-rehabilitation or chanting in a protest march on Capitol Hill. What differs is the momentary changes in activity within and between those dimensions and how they are manifest in interaction. In the flowchart below, I present my own thinking on how to guide actions, whatever the moment.

Matrix Thinking About Aims

The choice of format and aims in CoMT does not have to be complicated. For instance, it should be possible to use the same framework whether the person was in an individual session with functional goals or in an informal drop-in choir or political advocacy group; what would change is the way in which you had identified functional goals and cultural direction initially. Consequently, the style of your monitoring, reporting, and communicating might differ in focus, vocabulary, or application and the written descriptions of the goals and activities themselves (if they exist) would inform the reader of the work's values.

In another example, a person's emotional flexibility in an individual session may be quite different from when in a group or public workshop because of the social situation. This would have been a factor in the choice of session format initially, based on the priority of that dimension of the work and the wider needs and interests of the person. Your thinking would then give rise to a unique set of functional and interactive considerations in interpreting the analysis. The basic understanding in this approach is that the musical benefit in a given situation is seen in the interplay between a person's many active functions and in the interactive use of those functions, in the context of how the person presents in their real-life setting.

In the table below, I set out one way of thinking through aims and formats. Using a matrix presentation of how active a person (or group or community) is both functionally and interactively, the flowchart enables you to identify first in which dimensions they are most or least active. Then it gives space for you to decide whether you seek to address areas of low activity or enhance those areas of high activity. This simple process enables an easy way of considering the formats of work that might best suit your agreed aims. This review could be carried out by a lone music therapist in relation to an individual client or, equally, by a group of reviewers in relation to a larger group or community. The dimensions of activity that become most prominent will show you what the focus (tacit or explicit) of your work has been and will prompt consideration of your priorities and methods.

Date	Client / Group / Community
Review by	

Dimension	Functional Level			Interaction Level		
	Low	Mid	High	Low	Mid	High
Fin Motor (F)						
Gross Motor (G)						
Sensory (Se)						
Attention (A)						
Expression (Ex)						
Social Skills (So)						
Emotional (Em)						
Cognition (Co)						
Creativity (Cr)						

Most Active Dimensions

Least Active Dimensions

Agreed Aims	Suggested Formats/Activities

Fig. 4: Matrix of aims

Implications for Theory

Within the idea of a "matrix" of musical formats and a flowchart of aims is the idea that in musical experience the connections we make are somehow the same "material" as what flows through them. Or, put in another way, everything is (still) music. The musical material such as a tone or a song is a sounded emergence of structures that can also be understood musically: Sounding and organising musically are interconnected. In this way, the tone produced by a person with a severe brain injury can be understood through the same thinking as the march a person makes in a noisy political demonstration.

Typically, a matrix is defined as a mould, or a container, within which something else can be formed, grown, or dispersed. For my thinking, the container itself *is the production of*, and *carries,* musical experience, whether or not that comes into sound form. In different dimensions, emerging into different observable forms, along divergent but simultaneous routes, musical operations somehow connect people, their inner worlds, their interactions, and the cultural forms that surround them. This is how it is possible for music therapists to see musical operation occurring in multiple dimensions and in multiple time frames, yet in individual persons and at discrete moments.

Is it possible to reconcile multiplicity and unity? What conceptual models exist that can reflect this view of musical experience as both multiple and unified existing on an inner plane and in the social world, with meanings that are personal yet by definition shared? This section turns to the work of Deleuze and Guattari for assistance. Gilles Deleuze was a professor of philosophy at the University of Paris VIII and a key figure in post-structuralism. Felix Guattari was a psychoanalyst at the experimental La Borde Clinic in Paris, as well as a social theorist and activist. Together they wrote *Capitalism and Schizophrenia,* which consists of two books, *Anti-Oedipus* (1984) and the subsequent *A Thousand Plateaus* (1986). The collaboration of Deleuze and Guattari presents a joyful, pragmatic, and radical solution to the conceptual difficulties I have raised so far. The key theme here is rhizomic or "nomad" thinking, incorporating within it concepts of emergence and multiplicity. This section will not present an overview of the bewildering output of Deleuze and Guattari, but instead a discussion of a refrain in their work that is of practical relevance to unfolding the matrix model further. It is kept intentionally within their own philosophical world, referring out only when they do so themselves.

You may hear resonances in their own vocabulary and thinking with the literature from CoMT over the past 20 years.

Their first and main resonance with CoMT is the assertion that nothing can be considered in isolation:

> For the real truth of the matter ... is that there is no such thing as relatively independent spheres or circuits ... everything is production: production of production, of actions, and of passions; production of recording processes, of distributions, and of co-ordinates that serve as points of reference .... (2004, p.4)

Theirs is a philosophy of radical decentring. What we may frame as a "starting point" or an *a priori* statement, such as an objectively assessed clinical need, is in fact the production of an ongoing interconnected process. This suggests that the way we "know" something is always from the emerging, or "becoming" of a particular set of forces in a particular set of circumstances. These forces are in a constant "desire" state, toward new emergence, new becoming. This echoes the decentred, ecological approach to music, health, and personhood typical of CoMT.

Goodchild (1996) describes Deleuze and Guattari's philosophy as "a philosophy of desire" (p. 11). This is not to be thought of as referring to sexual drive or any other regular use of the term, but as an autonomous concept. Their philosophy of desire is one of "spontaneous, chaotic, and irreducible emergence" (p. 11), or the emergent properties of forces acting on themselves and each other. In Goodchild's summary, a revolution of desire would not aim to create a society of liberty, equality, and justice, but a society of multiplicity, desire, and creativity. It is a concept of *becoming*.

The translator's note in *A Thousand Plateaus* attempts to put into English a set of concepts that already had their own peculiar meaning in the original French. Chief amongst these is the concept of "nomad", or "rhizome" thought. This refers to forms that "do not reflect upon the world but are immersed in a changing state of things" (p. xiii). Nomad thought is open-ended, not driven only by singular aims. It is not linear and, notably, is not confined to philosophy, but in its organization makes new forms of philosophy out of art or social phenomena: "In fact, Deleuze and Guattari would probably be more inclined to call philosophy music with content than music a rarified form of philosophy" (p. xiv). Music is present throughout *A Thousand Plateaus*. Quotations from graphic scores are used as chapter headings, and a whole chapter is devoted to music as an ideal example of what they call rhizomic organization.

What Is a Rhizome?

Deleuze and Guattari's rhizome is a model of multiplicity: "any point of a rhizome can be connected to anything other, and must be ..." (2004, p. 7). This is contrasted with the model of the tree or taproot, which fixes along a linear order:

> A rhizome as subterranean stem is absolutely different from roots and radicles. Bulbs and tubers are rhizomes. ... Even some animals are, in their pack form. Rats are rhizomes. Burrows are, too, in all of their functions of shelter, supply, movement, evasion, and breakout. The rhizome itself assumes very diverse forms, from ramified surface extension in all directions to concretion into bulbs and tubers. (2004, p. 7)

The rhizome is connected, heterogeneous, multiple. There are no fixed points in a rhizome, only lines: "When Glenn Gould speeds up the performance of a piece, he is not just displaying virtuosity, he is transforming the musical points into lines, he is making the whole piece proliferate" (2004, p. 9). This has consequences, notably that even the number is not a universal concept measuring elements but itself has become a multiplicity. Units of measurement are replaced by varieties of measurement. Multiplicities are therefore defined by their line, by the "deterritorialization according to which they change in nature and connect with other multiplicities" (2004, p. 10).

The rhizome is a system that is not destroyed by rupture. When a rupture occurs in the system, it will start up again along another line of growth. In fact, there is a rupture in the rhizome every time a line of flight emerges, such as the sending up of a flowering stem from the root, but this line of flight is also part of the rhizome. In this way, music is an ideal of rhizomic behaviour: "Music has always sent out lines of flight, like so many "transformational multiplicities"—even overturning the very codes that structure or aborify it; that is why musical form, right down to its ruptures and proliferations, is comparable to a weed, a rhizome" (2004, p. 13). In its amenity to being modelled, the rhizome is a map with "multiple entryways" (p. 14). It is openness in all its dimensions.

To summarize the characteristics of the rhizome: The rhizome connects any point to any other point, even if its traits are not linked to similar traits; it is reducible to neither the one nor the multiple; it has neither beginning nor end, but always a middle from which it grows; it is constituted from lines, not points, which indicate its constantly changing nature; it "operates by variation, expansion, conquest, capture, offshoots" (p. 23); it is a map that is always in construction, with multiple entries and exits; it is nonhierarchical, it is "all manner of "becomings"" (2004, p. 24). It is liberating to know that there is a philosophical tradition considering the paradox that CoMT raises: considering the multiple within single points. The interconnected points of the matrix, the recognition of constant becoming, and the importance of non-hierarchies in the social structures of music therapy practice find a sort of home in this thinking.

Seeing Music as a Rhizome

Music, seen by Deleuze and Guattari, is a creative system, nonsignifying, able to free itself from precharted, or territorialized power. It returns throughout their work as an image of transversal unity (the phenomenon of unity within multiplicity). In other words, the operation of music is to re-create, seek newness, or reframe. For Deleuze and Guattari, musical "creations are like mutant abstract lines that have detached themselves from the task of representing a world, precisely because they assemble a new type of reality ..." (2004, p. 326). Music "affirms the power of becoming" (p. 327).

Much of the underpinnings of Deleuze and Guattari are based in power struggle. Their work is tied directly to the politics on the streets of Paris and to specific settings: the university, the psychiatric clinic. They posit a philosophical world concerned with the relationship between forces, bodies, organizational systems, and territories, with the intention of reframing hierarchies and traditional roots of power. Into this, music is placed not as a destabilising influence, but as a system that can in fact reterritorialize, revisiting its own stuckness or chaos and "remusicing" it. Perhaps this is what CoMT desires: something that can reterritorialize health, revisit stuckness in our work, and—hopefully—remusic us.

Toward Context

The concept of rhizomic organization leads us to reconsider our models of context. I have so far suggested that formats and aims can be considered to emerge out of our systemic thinking about music, need, and people. Now this formulation of formats and aims points to a similarly decentred notion of context. I have suggested that the format in which we offer music therapy is one of our natural professional choices; music is a property of social experience that can be shaped and adapted. Within that, music therapists make choices about how to work, what to work toward, when to allow, and when to aim. I have suggested a matrix diagram and flowchart as possible guides to thinking and action. There is also now the idea that if practice is the manifestation of these emergent elements, CoMT both is produced by contextual aspects and impacts productively upon them. This is a constant theme in CoMT literature and an integral part of practice. In the next chapter, I will explore this theme through the story of "Pam" and her musical theatre work, "JUNK".

Chapter 6

MATRIX OF CONTEXT

"Pam" in Context

The subject of this chapter is a person in a context, inspired by music therapy with Pam. Geographically, we are still in our large care home in southern England. This care home is part of a large private health care company, subject to all the forces or commerce and culture that typify care in the UK. All of this (and more) is an equal subject for this exploration. The chapter builds on the idea that our formats and aims are in turn part of a wider context of professional practice. We, too, along with the client, are also contributing factors in characterizing that context. I will suggest in this chapter that what we usually call the "context" is not at all confined to place, people, or physical objects; it is all those plus an array of desires, agendas, and interests that swarm between.

Pam's story resonates with Caryl's. Pam's music therapy saw her progress from improvisation, piano exercises, and songwriting into a project involving members of the whole organization, culminating in a theatrical performance by members of her care home, their family, and directors of the company and a music therapy charity. The diversity and also the reach of our music therapy formats created widely dispersed aims in practice. The chapter will trace how music therapy changed throughout a complex context and also how it impacted upon it.

The Context of Care Homes

There are over 20,000 care homes in the UK, forming a major part of health care provision for people living with long-term chronic illness, particularly the dementias and neurological disability. I have worked as a music therapist in this context for over 15 years, and I am fascinated by how it combines clinical (i.e., medical and nursing) and cultural (i.e., psychosocial) models. In care homes, clinical nursing and medical health care are situated within a domestic, social environment, with a person-centred ethos. CoMT continually has to negotiate this sense of co-existing values and orientations. Both the care home company featured here and its collaborating specialist music charity are motivated by a desire to care well, but both are also embedded in industrial, commercial environments. These factors create a particular set of values that contribute directly to the content and focus of CoMT.

According to the *Care Quality Commission Report (2014–15)*, there are 15,186 care homes registered for adults in England. This figure includes nursing homes and homes without nursing. Although the language of registration refers to older people and dementia in its nursing care statistics, other research suggests that it is more difficult to establish the precise clinical details of people who live in care homes.

Care homes in the UK are professionalised environments. Whilst they are underpinned by the clinical practices of professional nursing care, they operate according to a social model, under the values of Person-Centred Care. The UK NICE-SCIE Guidelines on Dementia Care describe Person-Centred Care as an approach concerned with "looking for the person" so that people living with illness can be "treated as individuals with a unique identity and biography and cared for with greater understanding" (2006, p. 72).

In this way, the "clinical" is often apparently accessed via the "cultural". It is a natural place for musical work, as one of many psychosocial practices, to take a normalized form. The development of the "communal" approach to musical work in the UK has been advanced significantly by the care home setting, owing in part to this unusual need to approach the "clinical" values of health care via the "cultural" values of person-centred care.

Care homes not only are driven by clinical, cultural, and communal values, but also are maintained by, and often run for the purpose of, commercial interests. Whether put in terms of cost effectiveness or profit, it is clear that a consideration of how funds are spent and how they can be managed or optimized creates an *industrial* element in the ecology of care homes. They are independent organizations, operating in a changing commercial context, where the question of funding is a constant preoccupation. This question of funding is located increasingly in the choice of services offered for residents, rather than only in the assessments and treatments provided. I have learned that where the ecology of music therapy is made of cultural, clinical, communal, and industrial forces, the practice itself will be influenced and structured from those forces, too.

"JUNK"

The Starting Point

Pam referred herself to music therapy with the certainty that characterised everything she did. Pam had seen me working musically with others in the home, and I had a comfortable rapport with her. She had lived independently all her life, but now the limiting effects of her multiple sclerosis had required her to sell her own property and move to a care home. Pam's mind was keen and razor-sharp. Her physical life, however, was severely limited. Chronic pain, discomfort, and fatigue left her frustrated, isolated, and angry. Like Caryl, Pam refused to give in, developing an attitude of protest in relation to the limitations of her disease.

Pam used to play the piano and had enjoyed writing poetry in the past. Again, like PJ and Caryl, Pam wanted music therapy to show her *"what she could still do"*. We began with piano, simple percussion instruments, and vocal explorations. Pam's fatigue levels meant that her best playing or singing was always in the first two minutes, so we had to "hit the ground running" and establish a sense of achievement immediately, with no time wasted. In response to these conditions, I wondered if there was a way to keep an improvisational attitude but use the musical activity of specially composed piano exercises. Pam liked this idea. I started to write piano exercises aimed at drawing her skills out slowly, thinking about posture, hand extension, coordination, beauty, expressiveness, and strength.

The Context of a Body

A person's music is formed first in the context of their own body. Pam's musical drive was continually in negotiation with obstacles such as her own strength and changing fatigue levels. The varying skills and tendencies of the body present not only natural formats and aims, but also a physical context for practice. They impact upon schedules, as well as configurations of furniture, rooms, and instruments. This body context is also a mind context. Even within small piano exercises, I was presented with the choice of reflecting a functional or psychosocial standpoint. Framed musically, Pam in this mind-body context could be a different Pam.

The Context of a Project

Echoes of earlier work clanged into my mind when Pam voiced her frustration by saying, *"I feel like I've been thrown on the scrap heap of life"*. Certainly, the onslaught of MS meant that she could do far less than she used to and with far less independence. The second meaning for me was that having to live in a care home meant to her that she was in a kind of "ghetto": For Pam, care homes were a "scrap heap" for people who had lost their use. I could see what a devastating impact this attitude could have, and although I didn't share that belief, it was tangible and real every day for her. I found myself responding: *"Right, well that's where we'll go, then. We'll go to the scrap heap and do our music there."*

Assisted by the home's activities organiser, and our health and safety officer, we carefully arranged a trip to the local scrap yard. There we were helped to source objects safely that interested Pam. Perhaps influenced by the Scrap Metal Project previously, I imagined she might be motivated by what they could sound like when played as percussion. I was wrong. Pam saw the objects as metaphors for her own state. She gave human characteristics to them. We came back from our trip with a vacuum cleaner, the inside of a mattress, some television parts, and some copper pipes.

Over the next six months, Pam began writing song lyrics in the voice of these and other scrap items. She imagined that the vacuum cleaner was a lovesick man and that the mattress was an amorous young teenager, creating more characters and linking them with song styles that she enjoyed. We collaborated each week on turning her lyrics and song interests into new works, inspired by her own preferences. As those took shape, a plot emerged that would link these songs into a musical product.

Pam's process had begun with brief expressive moments at the piano, in which she tested her own functional level and took steps toward being communicative and creative within a less self-critical attitude. Our context had been Pam herself, in relation to me, within the relatively small range of the care home. The act of visiting the scrap yard and subsequently arriving at a songwriting process with an emerging theatrical narrative changed all that. It caused the aspects of her musical life to proliferate, consequently expanding the scope of our music therapy context.

Within each moment of lyric-writing, even in her thoughts as she went to sleep, perhaps, there was both the momentary structure of a musical event and the ongoing development of a new musical awareness. This was a marvellous context of musical activity. Pam's process was by now impacting on other staff members and residents in the home. They too were becoming interested in her ideas and part of the process. In addition to the personal context, a shared professional context was emerging, along with a cultural strand related to Pam's active musical imagination. I felt as a music therapist that for me to keep a professional awareness of this array of activity, I had to accept the discomfort of it not all fitting together yet. In fact, I thought that the life of the work was exactly where it seemed most problematic.

Creating a New Context

Soon Pam had made a sophisticated musical product. Her story described five scrap items: a TV, a mattress, a vacuum cleaner, a sink and a dustbin. They "lived" in a scrap yard that was owned by a mean, ungenerous man. His neglect of them was a consequence of his own dissatisfaction with life. He spent his time getting drunk, whilst they secretly fell in love, flirted, and argued. At his lowest moment, when he was desperate, he realised that he could hear the objects talking. They had been watching him all along, and they were angry. In his moment of need, they join together, and he discovers that his true vocation, to be an artist, can be realised if he sees them differently: not as useless objects, but as equal partners and able to help him. The piece ends with him changing the scrap yard into a gallery and transforming the objects into sculptures.

Pam asked if this could be performed in the care home. Firmly, she said, *"I want staff to perform it"*. She named two people for whom she had written parts. They both agreed. I then saw the possibility of taking senior figures from the organizations involved and giving them roles, both as scrap objects and also as the "bad", mean-spirited owner. To our delight, everyone we asked auditioned for Pam, passed, and agreed to rehearse and perform the project. Pam had instigated the creation of a new context, which slowly became a theatrical company for that event. Pam's process had become identified in a wide range of products—and now a production. Each week during this time, I met with her to report on any steps of which she had not been part herself, playing her recordings of rehearsals, checking the printed material, and keeping her involved.

Pam was now more of a writing partner than a typical client. In fact, we were both part of a company in the theatrical sense, focused on a future performance event, with a project to complete. The work involved us all making decisions and judgements and maintaining a shared creative vision over time. Now the project had a lot more people invested, each of them risking something in the process. Although they were not clients in the strict sense, I was accountable to them, and they to me, in different ways.

It was also clear that the successful production and its recording and subsequent editing into a DVD were translations of an initial musical impulse into vastly different materials, each bearing a different connection to the original music source. We had not created simply a list of functional interactive "outcomes". We had created an array of new material forces, each one a translation of Pam's musical work. That array included a DVD, an edited training resource to be distributed in the company, staff morale, company cohesion, a sense of the completion of an endeavour, brand identity, corporate value, good PR and corporate records in the charity's Annual Review, and, at the core, a feeling of completion for Pam.

The Context of (a) Company

By now, there were many ways in which the processes and outcomes of "JUNK" could have been evaluated. Over the course of the project, which now covered more than 18 months, musical work had elicited in Pam greater fine motor control via piano playing and handwriting lyrics, enhanced attention and concentration, more co-creativity, a musical partnership, a sense of purpose and motivation, cultural engagement, improved relations with staff, family reconciliation, and personal pride in completion of the project. We had also created an array of new materials, including a DVD, an edited training resource to be distributed in the company, increased staff morale, more company cohesion, a sense amongst many of the completion of an endeavour, new brand identity, and good PR material for the company and for the collaborating music therapy charity, Nordoff Robbins.

Such an expansion in scope generates a similar expansion in contextual influence. The work stands to impact upon, and be influenced by, a much more explicit and diverse set of interests. When staff training, or advocacy, or performance projects become part of CoMT, the participants go through their own process of change. What is the difference between a stakeholder, a supporter, a beneficiary, and a client? My experience in the context of care homes and of the health care professions is that a large number of people allow themselves to be changed by music therapy.

Music and Organizations

Discourses of Health Care

Inspired by my experience with "JUNK" and by the insights our work generated into this wider context, I set up a study to explore further. I wanted to find out of what this context actually consisted. What did people mean when they drew those concentric circles of the client, plus the therapist, plus the family, the building, the town ... and more important, what did I mean? I was granted generous permission to bring this enquiry back into the same care home organization and Nordoff Robbins as a doctoral research project, so that I could ask this question more systematically. I was allowed to explore care homes where music therapy happened, to talk to staff, residents, and families. Beyond that, I talked to senior company and charity directors and examined official marketing and communication documents. Here was my main line of investigation:

What is the range of the network created
by evaluation of CoMT?

I already had supposed that this professional context involved the interrelation of a large number of aspects. I also recognized that those aspects are not all of the same order. That is, some aspects are concrete physical elements such as files, computers, walls, and chairs. Other aspects are less concrete, such as professional standards, company expectations, or timing. Aspects such as these are not as fixed as material objects are; they may be pervasive assumptions or policies or the emergent properties of the interrelation between material aspects. All the same, those many aspects created different types of meaning in relation to one another. Finally, I had suspected that this context covered a large territory not only geographically, but also in terms of reach across sectors, types of knowledge, and readership.

This thinking led me to discover three ways in which context was created by CoMT. They were by direct contact with music, by sharing across the organization, and by public dissemination or broadcast. Each way involved interaction via diverse discourses. These three ways served to create the complex context in which music therapy with Pam took place. The following section describes the journey I took around the context created by CoMT. It lists the discourses that appeared to carry information about this context, describing some of the conversations I had and things I saw during my investigation. First, it will describe how I saw people making meaning from their direct contact with music in music therapy. Then it goes on to explore how people one step removed, yet still within the organization, gave meaning to it. Finally, it looks at how information is disseminated and broadcast beyond the organization. I write this in the style of an ethnographer, hopefully sharing some of the feeling of discovering these elements for the first time.

Direct Contact with Music

I found five main discourses that were active at the level of direct contact with music. They were:

- Personal Biographical
- Professional Music Therapy
- Dementia Care
- Design/Layout
- Sales

In the sections below, I present field notes and discussion regarding how people make contact with the music of CoMT and through what discourses they create meaning about that contact.

Discourse 1: Personal Biographical

On entering a care home, the first encounter with CoMT is what can be heard coming from around the corner from the foyer. A housekeeping assistant is singing along to the sounds of a music therapist who is with a resident, himself out of sight from her. I notice how she is dressed: in a uniform, but a uniform subverted with badges and hair clips. The housekeeping assistant seemed to use the presence of the music therapist to support her own stance on how care work should be. She connected the music therapist to her own beliefs about music, saying, "I myself love music, it creates an atmosphere of happiness". She also enjoyed being included in his world, noting that the music therapist "invites everyone in". This sense of inclusion was echoed by other staff members, such as the maintenance man who recounted how "music therapy makes me join in".

Musical experiences within CoMT seem to connect with the

personal and biographical, extending out from and into the personal histories of people who have direct contact with it. The resident who is overheard by the housekeeping assistant, and whose life already is summarised in formal documents such as a care plan, is perceived to be personally involved in the creation of this moment, witnessed by care staff who find it important that "[the resident is] … taking it all in—concentration, facial expression, reminiscence, past thoughts …".

It seems that staff members who hear or view this work connect it primarily with the personal biography or an emotional state in the resident. They seek to see change in residents' state and proof of impact and value the notion that "everyone can benefit". This perceived personal connection between music and residents is also connected with how care staff think about residents' preferences. They note that the music therapist appears to make music that is congruent with residents' real interests: "They want to play, compared with when entertainers in general come".

The musical context is created not only in the shared time frame of what is on the lounge clock. Observers intuit that this musical moment is leading participants into or from other times or memory states. The context of CoMT is both synchronic and diachronic: The experience of making music in one moment might draw people in from other imagined times, or it may lead them into other mutually shared or indeed further idiosyncratic time frames. The effect of this orientation extends into family relationships, allowing people to maintain and enjoy connections. As the spouse of one resident put it, *"Music has been an enormous part of our lives before, and to have it as something now is really lovely. Something we can do together; you can't help it."*

Discourse 2: Professional Music Therapy

On one visit to a care home, I was able to film a music therapy session with the informed consent of the resident participating. An extract of the session film was edited for the purposes of analysis. The film extract and microanalysis were then used as subject matter for interviews with the music therapist and company director of care and quality, after the care home visit. I later spoke with the music therapist whilst he was filling in a standard music therapy evaluation form to report on his work with the resident who had been observed, Mr. N.

An evaluation form is an organizational device designed to store highly selective information regarding resident experiences. It involves a specialist translation by the music therapist from his/her musical experience with the client into a professional music therapy discourse. This discourse requires information with specific criteria. The elements given space in the standard evaluation form are:

- Resident's name
- Resident's unit or community and room number
- Session date
- Session venue
- Session type
- Reasons for referral
- Type of modality of engagement
- Musical themes or vocal range
- Rating scale used
- Level of resident on rating scale
- Date of next review
- Music therapist's name
- Musical communicativeness (7 levels, according to Nordoff Robbins scale)
- Client-therapist relationship in Coactive Musical Experience (7 levels, according to Nordoff Robbins scale)
- Main areas of work indicated
- BNRI Scale 1: Responses in low awareness state (5 levels)
- Main areas of work indicated

The music therapist is required to fill in boxes, using written text for some and musical notation, ticks, or circles for others. He/she is also required to give a summative description of the ability of the resident in musical experience, which is given a corresponding numeric value. The form is in three sheets of paper, giving opportunity for residents who are in low awareness states to be described using the same evaluation form. In this form, an engagement that is packed with meaning is summarised for organizational purposes into a small array of ticks, words, and codes. Information appears to be drawn from contrasting sources; biographical, medical, organizational (i.e., corporate systems), phenomenological, functional, observational, empirical, speculative, or causal.

Whilst the surface of the document makes use of standard topographical features (the box, the stave, the ladder), its theoretical topography is radically different, requiring empirical worlds (in the assumptions of medical practice and the professional identification of therapeutic goals) to coexist with more speculative aspects such as appraisals of ability or the identification of what the form calls "areas of work". The more implicit perceptions that occur within music therapy encounters are in some ways acknowledged, but the form calls for them to be communicated using standard professional terminology.

At periodic moments, a music therapist can be required to write detailed reports of his/her work. These are expected by professional audiences to carry the range of summative information about all or any aspects of the music experience that are relevant to the resident's benefit. During my second care home visit, a report was made available as an example of this. It was interesting to note the number of types of information included. The list is as follows:

- Diagnosis
- Age
- Number of sessions attended
- Dates
- Referrer
- Reasons for referral
- Habitual social tendencies
- Habitual physical/cognitive tendencies
- First impressions
- Personality
- Apparent cognitive understanding/insight
- Physical coordination
- Ability to regulate movement
- Confidence, self-assurance, self-criticism
- Ability to follow prompts/commands
- Breathing rate
- Vocal control, confidence, pitch range, flexibility
- Therapy goals—'psychosocial' and physical
- Session format
- Ability to imitate, range of independence of expression
- Relaxation, openness
- Musical strategies and techniques in support of goals
- Resident's response/impact of techniques, greater use of L hand, for example
- Resident's changing or emerging musical world—preferences,

abilities
- Detail in musical evidence—new pitch range, giving values, for example
- Consideration of some reasons for success
- Transferable or generalised skills/impact—not asking for cigarettes after MT sessions, for example
- Recommendations for future based on impact of current strategies

The report had a circulation list and a specific writing tone. It can be inferred from the circulation list and the tone of the writing style that the readership of the document is professional, multidisciplinary, and moderately informed. The readership of this gathering of evidence could include:

- Resident
- Care team
- Nurses
- MDT
- Home management
- Family members
- New care team in new home
- Care managers
- Consultants
- Music therapy supervisor

The diversity of professional readership is apparent in this document. A report is a representation of the resident and his process, the music therapist and his/her skills or achievements, and the relevance of music therapy itself to health care. It acts both as a record of experience and as a performed statement of professional music therapy discourses to an unnamed readership. Music therapy professional discourse is a skilled and multifaceted translation of a complex musical encounter into easily understood language that represents professional validity to a wide readership. Whilst that language is predominantly descriptive rather than interpretative, it has a set of jargon terms or commonly used parameters that communicate, or perform, professionalism to the report's readers.

Discourse 3: Dementia Care

Hidden from the view of visitors is the care plan entry, written by the music therapist about each encounter with a resident. It is a document that contains a direct translation of the music therapist's thoughts about the experience, usually completed within the same day as the experience itself. The entry in this care plan must be brief and be understood by people with little or no knowledge of music therapy. This translation requires the music therapist to summarise their musical experience and put it into words that relate to concepts generally understood within dementia care. The care plan relates only to experiences with the resident. It is common in dementia care for practice to involve families and friends, although that encounter is more difficult to incorporate into care plan formats.

The involvement of families and friends in CoMT practice can be understood within the values of dementia care. In one care home, I spoke with the activities organiser for more insight into the involvement of families and friends. She noted how it is often the family taking the initiative to attend events, making their own use of CoMT: *"Sometimes relatives will bring their husband or wife in, just because they like it, and it doesn't matter if the person they've brought likes it."*

Discourse 4: Design/Layout

The impact of dementia care design and layout is illustrated in the audible and visible range of CoMT. First, music in this context is often heard before it is seen, as described by the housekeeping assistant who notes, *"We hear him down the corridor, it all travels, you hear people singing with him"*. Care homes are not soundproofed environments. This care home is in a typical courtyard layout with long, interlinked corridors; music in care homes can often be heard by strangers. To be able to hear a resident singing is to hear them being different from usual. The physical configuration of this network alters throughout the day, as the residents move, staff change location, and the music therapist brings his music to different people in different spaces.

The physical location of encounters with CoMT is not fixed; its focal points change according to where the music therapist or the resident is, and its spread changes according to the layout of the home, fire doors, other competing sound sources, or the receptivity of staff to hear and respond to what is being created. For example, the housekeeping assistant hears from afar a musical moment between the music therapist and a resident. She is at that time in the right physical location, with the right confluence of circumstances, for her to take in, and co-create, that musical moment in connection with the music therapist and the resident. There is a simultaneous interpenetration between the physical environment, her direct perception, and her own sense of what that means to her, for her own biography. In this way, it can be suggested that the physical features of a location can impact discursively on the listening or viewing of the people in the location. When the housekeeping assistant hears a musical moment, she is surrounded by other objects such as specially designed furnishings, ornaments, or pieces of equipment, and each contributes to what she must make of this musical experience. These have been around her for as long as the music therapist has been working there. They are not a secondary piece of evidence for her; they exist as part of the context in which she translates what she is hearing. The texts on the walls, posters, timetables, and juxtapositions of music therapy text with other documents produce a third, emergent impression, characterising CoMT and impacting upon her description of its value.

The context of CoMT is also textual: Information about it is woven into text objects that are not typically considered part of CoMT in everyday care home life, such as activities timetables, and thus are out of the music therapists' direct control. It is translated into activities jargon and into a discourse associated with general dementia care. It then has to compete for visibility with other translations. In this sense, the range of the network does not have strict borders in language. Apart from the written verbal texts that signify and explain or give clues as to what music therapy may be, other texts abound, too. The furniture of music therapy in the care home acts as a text, read by onlookers and creating a particular version of how the experience can be understood.

Discourse 5: Sales

In private health care, direct contact with music can also effect sales, via a combination of personal and commercial discourses. The sales and marketing manager's encounters with prospective residents and families is commercial, yet it is mediated within personal, biographical information: *"... they will then talk: 'oh, yeah, my dad used to play the violin', or something like that ..."*. I ask her why music therapy seems so important here: *"I think music therapy is something that will make people sit up and listen, not because they understand it fully, but because it's music".* It appears from this that part of the music therapy encounter is a level of musical experience that is arresting, capturing onlookers' attention and communicating something perhaps essential to them, about the values of the home. When that identification occurs, the musical experience generates a sales potential in visitors or onlookers.

Sharing Across the Organization

After the initial direct contact with music, a second level occurs, where context is created via integration with organizational structures, from written, photographic, or verbal accounts into new relations with other discourses. These new relations generate new processes and values. This was most clearly illustrated by interviews with senior care home staff and company/charity directors. The discourses that created this level of context were:

- Sales
- Display
- Cinema
- Music Specialism
- Nursing
- Training
- Management
- Health Care Culture
- Health Care Business Practice

Discourse 5: Sales

The direct encounter with music therapy has commercial outcomes when it extends not only to families but also to medical consultants by word of mouth. The sales and marketing manager also notes that there is both a purposeful element in CoMT, as she can use its value in her sales work, and a basic relevance and value for residents in everyday life.

Discourse 6: Display

One way in which CoMT contributes valuably to sales is the use of photographic images. My first observation on viewing one care home was that the images of music therapy in the reception area are of a particular type. These are not "rough and ready". They are journalistic. The standard of the mounted photographs is professional, using the style of photojournalism, with a particular sense of display about them. The photographs capture more than simply a figure, instead giving the viewer a sense of place and personality. These pictures of music therapy in action tell a story and are given prime locations on the walls of the home.

Discourse 7: Cinema

My journey around this context suggested that that the habits and expectations of what I call "cinema" can impact upon the context of CoMT. I used a film extract as a memo device for an interview with the director of care and quality. Unlike journalistic photographs that seem to be direct records of a moment, edited film extracts from CoMT sessions transfer information that has been processed more strategically. Film is a form that communicates richly with a viewer. The 30 minutes of musical experience in a care home become reduced and characterised on editing after the event. The edit becomes separated and offered later on an unspoken understanding that the smaller extract will stand for something larger, containing in it an indication of the whole, unseen, encounter. In this way, the range of the network relies on discourses that relate to cultural expectations, or habits of viewing and storytelling, that are generally associated with the cultural heritage of cinema.

The range of the context opened up by film and cinema is increased further by the use of digital social media. Potentially by the evening of a CoMT session, a film of the encounter might have been edited and posted in an envelope to anywhere in the world or onto a corporate website or Tube-style free-content video site or tweeted to users around the globe—and viewed that same day. The range of the network begins to seem, in geographical terms, almost unlimited. Digital film is an innovation that opens up 90 seconds of time to a vast world of broadcast, viewership, interpretation, and dissemination.

Discourse 8: Music Specialism

A second device, a microanalysis of a 90-second film extract, was used to offer the director of care and quality a contrasting translation of musical experience. I was given permission to observe and film a session in a shared social space in a care home. Mr. N. was a resident living with Parkinson's disease. He was able to give informed written consent to my presence in the lounge whilst he sang with the music therapist and to being filmed for a short time. He was suggested for filming because he had capacity to give informed consent, and he took a conversational interest in what the music therapist was doing. The extract of the music therapist working with Mr. N. details a brief moment in time but draws on wide-ranging discourses, making links between split-second changes and an array of motivating factors from diverse material, theoretical and aesthetic worlds.

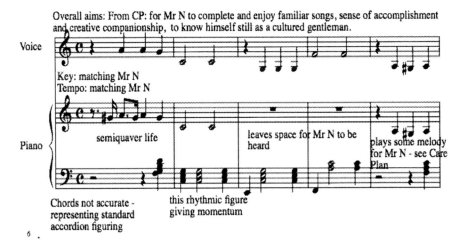

Fig. 5: Extract of microanalysis

My commentary in the microanalysis touches the specialist world of musical cultures in its necessitating the use of notation. At the same time, it connects the musical structures to health care questions about symptoms. This implies that the range of the network touches on areas with a vastly different methodology and language. Along with the film extract, it was offered to the director of care and quality (DoC) as a trigger for discussion about how he understands the value of CoMT.

His surprise when I (SW below) offered him sheet music as a form of representation of music therapy was striking:

> SW   So the next thing I want to show you is …
> DoC Sheet music?
> SW   Yes! (introduces it … shows score and describes)

> DoC So he's singing the top bit … and this is the accompaniment? From my feeble knowledge I would say that the guy's still pretty intact … is the accompanist playing the correct tune? He's following it all pretty well, isn't he? To look at this, he's still got a lot of ability left, and a lot to give … so without reading whatever's here, I would say that the guy's engaged with it. He's obviously not able to do the whole thing, 'cause there's space left …

As the discussion unfolded, it became clear that each different form of evaluation or reporting presented a very different impression of the resident, Mr. N. It is possible that the specialist forms of music therapy analysis, and the use of music notation in that analysis, create not only a more positive impression of the practitioner (by demonstrating often-hidden skills and awareness), but also a more positive impression of the client.

Discourse 9: Nursing

The director of care and quality (DoC below) was shown four pieces of evidence from care home 1: a copy of a care plan for Mr. N., an evaluation form for Mr. N., the microanalysis of Mr. N.'s film extract, and the film extract itself. He was asked to comment on what these items told him about the work. His first observation in reading the care plan was that the resident is described as being able to give his opinion, to take pleasure, and to voice criticism of the music therapist. This evidenced, for him, a sense of "personhood", taking priority over other areas, such as physical treatment of the body, for example. He was unclear as to whether CoMT can extend into functional purpose. It is striking that CoMT may in the formal perspective of the health care company impact only on the level of pleasure. The care plan did not indicate diagnosis and thus did not show that the music therapist was engaging with function.

The care plan information did not give a direct indication of diagnosis or pathological symptoms. When that information was eventually provided to the director of care and quality, it generated a much more detailed and animated discussion. He seemed surprised that music therapy evaluation could touch on this dimension. This may be an indication of the difficulties of representing information fully within the organization or perhaps also of the focus of corporate and health care cultures. He also wondered if other staff could learn something from the music therapist's evidence, if they could enrich their own work through music therapy.

Care home staff do have opportunities to encounter information about music therapy practice, albeit often as a second translation. This happens primarily via the care plan. The care plan is kept in a large green lever arch file, in a special cupboard, in a special room known formally as the "Nurses' Station". This is an official legal record of the care given to each resident and is completed continually throughout the day. The network here is maintained by physical mobility; the file can be lifted, carried, copied, and shown to any visitor with clearance to view notes. This illustrates that the range of the network created by CoMT extends beyond the time it occurs and beyond what is audible, as many nursing and care staff may not witness musical experiences directly.

Discourse 10: Training and Development

The strongest indication of the director of care and quality's interest in the value of CoMT was how this knowledge is shared with care staff. He noted that the written evidence does not direct other care staff to use musical insights in their own care giving, such as rhythmic walking with a resident living with Parkinson's disease. The success of knowledge sharing, or transfer, with staff around a large organization seems to depend on the ability for that organization's training systems to carry it. The enquiry led to an interview with the company's director of learning and development.

Regarding the question of whether the network of CoMT extends to the general workforce of the company, the director of learning and development (DoLD below) was tentative:

> SW ... that suggests to me that musical work with staff is sometimes very similar to the musical work with residents. We don't call it therapy, and the professional responsibilities are different ...
>
> DoLD Is that a good or a bad thing? I don't know ... Is that not just a label?

It is notable, then, that the context of CoMT seemed to extend beyond residents and staff in direct contact with music to out across the company. The director of learning and development also remarked that its value was best transmitted via "advocates". This insight was striking, as it implies that from a learning perspective, not only was it necessary for information to be translated at an organizational level, but also it was important for people themselves to promote and share the impact of the experience in parallel with that information.

Discourse 11: Management

In these examples, it seemed that CoMT touches, or has the potential to touch, on the lives of a workforce. In this context, that covers a geographical spread across the UK; it also reaches deeply not only to care staff but also to kitchen, hospitality or housekeeping, management, and support staff. The lens of management allows this practice and affords it an official reach. The value of CoMT in relation to management is captured in this quote from an interview with the managing director (MD):

> MD I think it is very good for our employees to witness what you're doing, to be part of it, they are highly participative, aren't they? ... and I think it's an absolute upbeat part of their job that they can be part of this therapy process and actually see a manifest outcome to the benefit of the resident. So I think that's great, because in terms of motivating people, that must be a fundamental element of why they turn up for work every day.

Whereas in direct contact, the experience seems to be translated via microlevel translations, the managing director made assumptions from a greater distance. He supposed, perhaps from his own microlevel experiences, that experience of CoMT must be a practical motivation for the workforce. This assumption is made through an organizational lens and relates to staff as a collective notion as well as to individuals.

Discourse 12: Health Care Culture

Beyond the care home or company staff, the managing director's interest, on being asked about the value of CoMT, was in yet another group of interested people. I asked him to consider the transformational impact of CoMT by recalling his experiences as an audience member at the performance of "JUNK". I discussed the impact of "JUNK" on residents and staff, but he responded:

> MD I think the constituency that you missed was Pam's relatives, because they're very engaged, aren't they? … and they were the most thunderstruck by everything that had been created in "JUNK", and what it had done for their loved one, and it was a tremendous relief … to see their loved one being able to project and create and communicate, given the limitations of her position.

From this interview with the managing director, it emerged that families are regarded as a highly significant set of participating interests.

Discourse 13: Health Care Business Practice

The constituencies of interest that the managing director notes expand beyond the "nuclear" context of resident, family, and staff. He thinks beyond the care home and into how this work contributes to how the company is presented:

> MD If you take it a few steps further, yes, being able to spread the word, publicise the sort of work you undertake, and what actually happens within the four walls of one of the care homes, it has to be good for the image and reputation of that care home, and ultimately it must be good for impressing the views of commissioners and regulators.

At this point, the questions of publicity, image, and reputation emerged. These point to questions of mass readership, ways of organising information to an agenda beyond the record-keeping of health care systems or the training of a workforce and into the endeavour of creating specific marketing images for the purpose of convincing strangers of the value of this practice. Here it was suggested that CoMT extended via the outward-looking agenda of reputation and also inwardly, in relation to the workforce. In either sense, the range of the context reaches a set of operations that have no direct link with the music therapist and the resident, yet which seek to carry the force and personality of those musical encounters.

The challenge for CoMT is tracing the links between an event and a supposed consequence, where the practice is orientated either toward impact or toward causal outcome. On film, perhaps, it might be easier to create the appearance of direct causality, but at this range, where exchanges derived from CoMT are released into a workforce or large organization via film extracts or training initiatives, the ability to trace connections becomes problematic for the system.

Public Dissemination and Broadcast

At the point where information is in a form that can be disseminated, broadcast, or assembled for general consumption (such as a digital movie file), it appears that a third translation occurs. In this study, four main discourses were found to be active in this translation. They were:

- PR
- Mass Media
- Research
- Fund-raising

Health care information systems require numeric information that can be turned into statistics such as numbers of sessions per week. They also require stories, examples of successes, and evidence of the good practice of music therapists, their ethical conduct, and their music therapy approach.

Aspects such as concepts, films, accounts, tables of numbers, and performances are evaluative objects of multiple provenance, containing diverse types of information: speculative, summative, detailed, and generalised. They are versatile objects that have evolved or been innovated to serve desires and urges far beyond the musical encounter: the desires of a workforce, a company ethos, an entrepreneurial spirit, a sense of corporate governance, or the interest of a generalised readership.

Discourse 14: PR

PR materials are constructed to appeal to an array of readership types where many aspects of evaluative information are drawn together. This includes statistics, reviews, images, and branding. In one sense, publications containing PR materials are a confluence of many types of evaluative material into one object. They are layered with the various agendas, discourses, texts, images, and representations of CoMT.

Discourse 15: Mass Media

Sometimes, however, the performance of CoMT evaluation to mass readership evaluation is more specifically driven. In the case of preparing press releases on research reports, the task of translation is to move from an organizational level to a public level of impact. Email correspondence regarding the preparation of a press release on a research announcement offers a rich insight into this process of translation. This study was able to use an email correspondence containing striking examples of the processes through which evaluative material must pass in order to reach a general reader.

The purpose of the emails that are included as data was to prepare a document that would be sent to a large range of media organizations, with the intention of interesting them in creating a "news item" out of the information. One dimension of the range of the network, therefore, is that it occupies a territory of media or general language where the overriding concern is for unequivocal, causal, positive impact, as seen in this marketing correspondence: *"The important thing for me (and the only thing that will help us get coverage) is that it really clearly shows the specific positive impact music therapy can have on people with dementia."*

The demands of press agendas or the readership of news publications are that something clear and directly related to positive impact is provided. Press announcements demand a translation from one general approach of evaluation to another, according to readership.

Discourse 16: Research

The research intention in such situations seems to be to qualify the language used, rather than make firm causal claims. In the encounter between research discourse and PR or mass media discourses, research discourses appear to inform, explain, or propose; in contrast, it is the intention of PR discourses to claim, prove, and attract attention. An example of this is where a researcher correspondent qualifies what has been written in order to be accurate and avoid giving offence:

> check this rewriting—the previous version came across as
> though staff don't normally see residents as whole persons,
> etc. ... also, do check the last sentence—is it patronizing?

All the same, it seems difficult for researchers to remain
dispassionate when writing on this subject, as the following quote and
subsequent editorial comment from the researcher illustrates:

> Where someone can no longer speak, music therapists hear
> the music of their sounds and gestures ... drawing them
> into shared, intimate stepping together, music therapists
> connect people ...
>
> [the comment:] "GOT a bit carried away! Speaking to and
> from the heart...do modify as needed ...

The research discourse has contributed helpful catchwords and phrases to
the lexicon of mass media communications, as illustrated in this quote
from the ongoing draft being edited in the email correspondence: "Music
therapy not only affects the person with dementia, but enhances the entire
care setting, known as the "ripple effect"". The research discourse also
adds credibility, via the strategic use of quotes from experts.

The translation from research discourses to mass media
communication can be awkward. The correspondences on the ongoing
press release included comments such as:

> I felt a lot of it didn't make sense and was not written in
> plain English ...
>
> Is there a clear sentence/s we can include that explains
> HOW it works?
>
> I think we need a stronger case study than this ...

The evidence of numerous redrafts between research and
communications professionals is not evidence of poor command of
language or of the subject. It suggests instead that the act of redrafting
may be ineffectual if it only changes the words within the particular
frame in which it already exists. That is, this kind of redraft requires

that the information is shifted out of one discourse (research) and replanted in another (mass media communications). This appears to be not only a choice of words, but also a shifting of mind-set. This shift comes with its own power relation, between the discourses of research, PR, and mass communications and the professional discourse of music therapy itself.

Discourse 17: Fund-raising

Even within a charity, a fund-raising discourse is a commercial discourse that translates evaluative information into income. It uses representations via numeric values—quantities of work done, amounts of money raised or spent—and also aims to generate presence through images and storytelling (case study vignettes). Its techniques for achieving this are in the discourses it chooses to translate. It seeks to create the presence or represent the value of:

- Participating in music therapy
- Studying music therapy
- Hosting music therapy
- Donating money
- Being part of the charity

The action of this discourse is to invite a kind of membership, which has potential value for the charity. In this way, the Annual Review can link the housekeeping assistant who sings during her cleaning round with the pop star who sings at a charity concert as much as with the child who sings for the first time during her music therapy session.

The Range of Context

The range of the context created by CoMT seems to proliferate beyond the direct experience of music, the professional interests and concerns of the music therapist, or even the needs of the resident in the care home. It exists in a diverse set of discourses that span from diverse personal biographical interests to the anonymous dissemination of information for the general public. CoMT comes into visibility at the points at which parts of the context as a whole come into contact. In this sense, a part of the network can equally be a client, a music therapist, a piano, a vacuum cleaner, a report, a journalist, a DVD, a mood, a corporate ethos, a company director, and still more.

Paradoxically, the coherence of CoMT relies on a temporary flow of meaning through that network. CoMT seems to touch, or have the potential to touch, on the lives of a whole workforce. This covers a geographical "outreach" and also an "inreach" through not only care staff but also kitchen, hospitality or housekeeping, management, and support staff. The lens of learning allows this practice, and affords it, an official reach. From one perspective, this could be seen as a blurring of professional boundaries. Within that view, the encouragement of such a reach might risk being unethical. But within this system, it is viewed as an advantage, something to work with and celebrate, when moderated by the necessary professional considerations.

The constituencies of interest that are made visible in CoMT evaluation reach beyond the core of resident, family, and staff. They emerge as organizational interests affecting workforce morale, corporate identity, and branding. Here the role of publicity points to the likelihood of mass readership or viewership. This requires ways of organising information toward an agenda that goes beyond the record-keeping of health care systems, or the training of a workforce, and into the endeavour of creating specific marketing images for the purpose of convincing strangers of the value of something. This chapter suggests that CoMT could contain various kinds of currency for the company and the charity's benefit. The range of the network reaches a set of operations that have no direct link with the music therapist and the resident, yet which seek to carry the force and personality of those musical encounters.

Beyond the direct interpersonal contact and organizational information or training opportunities generated by CoMT, another translation occurs in the public sphere. A good example of this is when organizations publish documents such as annual reviews. The Nordoff Robbins Annual Review, for example, is constructed to appeal to an array of readership types. This is an example of Nordoff Robbins's public information output, where all information discourses are drawn together into an assemblage of numbers, reviews, images, and branding. As with any such text, this document is heavily layered with the various desires, worlds, texts, images, and representations of practice. The Annual Review is addressed to any reader who is interested in the work of the charity and of Nordoff Robbins.

Matrix of Context

Just as all the dimensions of a person are potentially present in musical experience, changing only with context, it seems that this array of interests and aspects of context is present across the context of CoMT. Whilst not active equally and simultaneously, each discourse may yet be co-active with another, depending on the context and circumstances of the evaluation process. When presented in a matrix format, the discourses that create context emerge as dynamic and interconnected. The lines drawn in the diagram below illustrate through one example what I propose could be a general principle. Here I suggest how the interrelation between discourses may have been performed when the housekeeping assistant was overheard by the researcher whilst she was singing with a music therapist during my first care home visit.

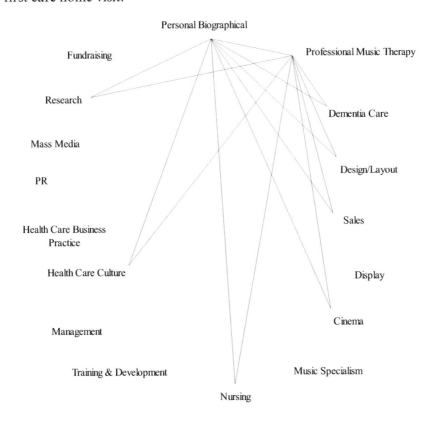

Fig. 6: Matrix of discourses

In this example, it is suggested that the discourses connected with lines are active when I encounter the housekeeping assistant singing with the music therapist. Those unconnected—such as Fund-raising, PR, or cinema— could be made active in other circumstances: if the same event were filmed for a promotional DVD, for example.

In this situation, elements such as health care culture, management, sales, and training were active, as they were seen by the participants to have been important. That is: The music therapist thought that staff participation was good for training, and he was thinking in a specialist musical way; the general manager saw benefits in it for management, sales, and health care culture; and the housekeeping assistant connected with it as part of her own personal biography. The researcher saw a link between the music therapist and the housekeeping assistant. The situation was enabled by specific design and layout features and by aspects of dementia care.

Implications for Theory

This chapter illustrates what the context of CoMT looked like to me over an eight-week period of research fieldwork. I used an approach from ethnography, Actor-network Theory, to frame my enquiry. This approach enabled me to consider how CoMT with people such as Caryl and Pam is a particularly dispersed kind of practice, reflecting a context of multiplicity in its own multiple structures. The next section discusses a theoretical approach to understanding this sort of picture: a large, rhizomic network of changing relationships, involving material processes, human interaction, and objects. It sets out an approach to performativity, drawing on Actor-network Theory to frame the discussion.

Performativity

Like all qualitative approaches in ethnography, the basis of Actor-network Theory (Latour, 1993, 2005, 2010) is the claim that meaning is embedded in context. Actor-network Theory stands out because it proposes that context is constructed by a network of what it calls "actors" that can be both human and nonhuman. The construction of meaning is seen as a paradoxical connection between the worlds of social construction (the multiple) and natural science (the reductive). Actor-network Theory suggests that "translation" reconciles these worlds, keeping incompatible parts of a context in connection. For Actor-network Theory, that translation is dependent on *performed* production of meaning. Law (2008) writes:

> There are two great views of method in science and social science. On the one hand, it is usual to say that methods are techniques for *describing* reality. Alternatively, it is possible to say that they are practices that do not simply describe realities but also tend to *enact* these into being ... the second approach...treats knowledge practices as more or less *performative*. (p. 1, underlining in original)

But what is being performed? This is not a reference to the importance of performing music, but instead a description of how reality is co-created. Other authors use different terms here to avoid confusion. Mol (2002), for example, uses the term "enactment" in place of performance. Actor-network Theory would argue that it is not only multiple meanings that are performed, but also realities. It is one thing to acknowledge that we come to know "the world out there" when we perform ourselves in it, but it is radically different to argue that our various performing creates the world variously: elements of the world themselves performing us, at each instance in a fresh and contrasting reality. In this sense, we might say that we are performed in tandem with the things whose existence we also perform.

Latour (1993) gives a perspective on how "things" co-create contexts and on how we can see a thread connecting the vast range of actors that comprise those contexts. This thread can be seen in the collections "of practices and instruments, of documents and translations ..." (1993, p. 121). The context is seen when controversies emerge in our awareness. It is when we notice change or ruption that we notice things and the connections between them.

In music therapy terms, these things could be as challenging as a YouTube video of a session and as apparently banal as a standard care home record form. In my process with Pam, the formal evaluation moments included process notes, index forms, care home records, and periodic evaluation forms. Informally, I would also include corridor conversations, her written notes to me, and the many objects that carried meaning about the performance project, including the event's programme, photographs, the DVD edit, and the "Thank You" cards we received after the show. The full picture of context is a complex translation across time between these and other elements.

Translation between elements in a context is an ongoing process made up of uncertain, fragile, controversial, and ever-shifting ties. If connections are visible, they are being *performed* and will generate new and interesting data. Where problems arise, Latour suggests, is where our attention should stay:

> ANT claims that it is possible to trace more sturdy relations and discover more revealing patterns by finding a way to register the links between unstable and shifting frames of reference rather than by trying to keep one frame stable ... ANT claims that we will find a much more scientific way of building the social world if we abstain from interrupting the flood of controversies. We, too, should find our firm ground: on shifting sands. (2005, p. 24)

The task of the researcher in Actor-network Theory is to render these associations traceable, and it might be said that the task of the theorist in CoMT is to do the same. This involves valuing the constructive role of all elements in the translation of meaning, even if they appear problematic. The paradoxical, uncomfortable, or provocative are not attractive because they are problematic, but rather because they must be concealing (or pointing to) something important.

This is an approach that technically allows us to consider at once the client and the context in which she is embedded. The points of translation in this particular context are of crucial importance. The translation between Pam's originating musical material and my emerging thoughts whilst playing, or between those thoughts and the process notes that occur moments later, have significance in co-creating the context we are in. Further, it is suggested here that our context remains coherent by material change: a material process of transformation from will to sound, musical organization to verbal meaning, and from verbal meaning into a proliferation of physical and conceptual objects. Only by trying to connect the elements that do not seem to work together can we discover the underlying connections between them, and perhaps bring ourselves closer to an understanding of music's multiplicity. As Latour would put it, "these sites are the shadow image of some entirely different phenomenon" (2005, p. 171).

Toward Evaluation

This chapter illuminates in some ways why evaluation is an issue in CoMT. The context of CoMT is multiple, producing formats and aims that are the manifestation of a multiple kind of knowledge. This context, through its many discourses, requires us to serve more than one kind of agenda. It is suggested here that in the process of sharing knowledge and information around a complex context, the value of practice can vary and distort. The concept of performativity accounts for how this creates multiple values. This in turn may affect how music therapy decisions are arrived at or obscured in practice and/or how a person's own musicality may start to reflect to the pervasive ethos of company performance or public relations.

The music of a context is not only in the sounds created by the music therapist and the client. It is (as Rumi's student discovered earlier) in the musicality of the co-ordination of multiple material flows carrying meaning between people and other elements, each in coordination with the other. At any point in this context, the flow of materials could be stopped and recorded, for the purposes of translation, encoding, and storage—that is, for evaluation. That moment of "stopping", where we pause everything to take stock, to evaluate, contains a paradoxical flow of multiple realities and possibilities. These can be a potent mixture of nameless, unknowable allowing, conscious, and measurable aims, interrelated desires, and complex discourses. The influence of one reality over another (of aesthetic over industrial, or professional over personal) will be determined by the interests of the person who wrote, and the person who reads, the evaluative material. In the next chapter, I explore some of the issues around evaluating CoMT, through the story of a young man called Paddy.

Chapter 7

MATRIX OF EVALUATION

"Paddy"

Clearly, one of the best things to ask of music is *"Show me what I can still do"*. PJ, Caryl, and Pam all came to me with that question, and in this story, the question is brought by a mother. *"Show me what my son can still do"* must be one of the more potent requests a music therapist can receive. In the early crisis months of a severe brain injury, it is more potent still.

For this story, we return to the neurological rehabilitation unit in the nearby hospital in southern England. As part of "From Therapy to Community", not only was I able to explore music therapy formats in community settings, but also I could also take referrals from the acute neurological ward of the hospital. Within the remit of developing a broad-based music therapy program that could meet people where they were, I had scope to work with individuals at the beginning of their assessment and recovery. When Paddy's mother, Mrs. S., contacted me, her son had only recently emerged from a coma, following a serious road traffic accident. In this chapter, I describe our work together, relating practice to the question of evaluation, offering a possible approach to assessment, and discussing some of the theoretical implications of performativity within CoMT.

Getting to Know Paddy

I first saw Paddy in his hospital bed. He was 19 years old, formerly a keen and accomplished rock musician, with a bright professional future. Now, Paddy carried the effects of multiple fractures, severe brain injury, and months of medical uncertainty. This uncertainty extended beyond simple medical facts and into Paddy as a person, too. Who was he, now, in this context? How could his family know him and rebuild their relationships with him after these months of devastation? In many ways, the effects of brain injury are to obscure a person, to cloud the channels of communication and interpretation. Perhaps this is what is behind the question we ask of music: *"Show me what my son can still do"*. In music, we know concretely: by doing.

The early stages of acute neurological rehabilitation involve a lot of instruments. Most of those are for medical assessment or part of nursing treatment. It still feels radical to bring a *musical* instrument into a place of medicine, especially when your mode of practice is music-centred, improvisational, and unplanned. It requires belief: in yourself, in the client, and in music. When I sat with Paddy for the first time, my guitar placed comfortably within his hearing, and plucked my first strings in time with his breathing, I was nervous. This was no performance in the normal sense, but it mattered as much as any other musical event would. Both Mr. and Mrs. S. were outside the room, observing through a window as I continued to play single guitar tones and sing low open vowels with Paddy's breathing.

My breathing entrained with him, then his fragile vocal tones entrained with mine, then our alternating voices transformed from reflex to response, from gesture to phrase. We were at work. By the end of the session, Paddy was showing me he could not only hear, breathe in time, and sing in tune, but also grip, beat, and count, too. It seemed as if points of certainty were emerging out of the mists. Those points were rhythm, tone, and turn-taking. Musical instruments showed us something that other instruments could not, Mr. S. putting it most powerfully afterwards when he said, *"You have brought our son's soul back"*.

During this early period of learning about Paddy, I worked within a neuro-rehabilitation frame, where I translated our musical experiences into vocabulary that my colleagues would find meaningful. I gathered information about aspects such as his ability to count beats and repeat them, his upper limb extension and proprioception, and his vocal strength and flexibility. This information was reported within a rehabilitative understanding of recovery, complementing reports from physiotherapy, occupational therapy, psychology and speech and language therapy. Paddy was still in a vulnerable state, requiring close 1:1 observation due to the troubling onset of epilepsy. So much information about him at this time was channelled through the medical gaze that his presence as a person was sometimes overtaken by his status as a patient.

From the beginning, however, in addition to this valuable information, I was also gathering knowledge. I was able to know Paddy in a way through music that was unique. And by observation and later participation, Paddy's family also were able to create knowledge about Paddy that was unique to them and to him. This is why multiplicity matters in CoMT. In music, a lot of things are going on at the same time, not only on a material level but also on a political and epistemological level. In that first session with Paddy, I was discovering information about him as a patient through a medical gaze, but also I was connecting with him profoundly as a person, through my own professional gaze. A third gaze, that of his parents, was also present, and powerfully. And what of his own perspective: Paddy showing himself what he can still do, in showing us.

Toward New Knowledge

Eventually, Paddy moved on from acute neurological rehabilitation in medical settings and came home. Under the terms of my CoMT project, I was able to continue working with him as a client. Now he was not under the close remit of a medical program, but was cared for at home by his family and a team of visiting professional carers, within an agreed health care package. The ongoing effects of epilepsy, short-term memory loss, and physical dependency meant that Paddy's functional and interactive world remained limited. The scope of his social life remained within the four walls of home.

Consequently, the task of CoMT in this situation remained wondrously multiple. Every week, I visited Paddy and we made music together in whatever way he was able to. By now, he was regaining many of the charming traits he had shown as a young man before the accident. He was kind and curious about people's lives, especially about their musical tastes. His were still firmly rooted in rock music. In reflection of my role as a health care professional, I found ways both to translate my rehabilitative imperative into satisfying musical experience with Paddy and to translate what we did into useful information for professional communication. Whilst much of our work was of course unseen by anyone except him and me, there were moments when Paddy wanted to show off, and in those moments we were able to translate his musicality into new and important knowledge for his family.

Paddy was also by now translating his experiences into verbal reflections. It was encouraging to see just how much he was learning about himself and about what he could be in music. First, there were insights about the basic process of recovery:

> ... in the past, I couldn't talk, and now I can sing an octave.
> I think about that when I sing. It makes me happy ...

Beyond this, Paddy also demonstrated his self-awareness and his ability to monitor himself whilst playing:

> ... you don't need to use all your muscles to play. You need to measure the amount of muscles and effort you put in. You have to be aware of the music and the energy you are putting into it. It's like knowing the world around me, and what's happening. Because when I'm playing, I've got to concentrate on the world; my brain thinks, "there's a pulse here", and makes my body be a part of the pulse ...

Claiming ownership of his body, and command of himself in the world, is a huge step for a young man who was so devastated by the effects of brain injury. This advance in his insight and reflective ability went a step further when he occasionally dictated free-form poetry, like this example, seeming to be a direct account of his sense of himself at the time:

Togetherness

In the arid wasteland
Having to start something new
On a blank canvas
A new life-form is born
With love and no scorn
Where there is peace and no war

I live in peace and there is no hate
Or scorn to feel love is your fate
A life-form to evolve
Takes a love union
Can unite the world's cultures
And the only thing is love

Music's effect, even within this microcosm, was to make conceptual and feeling-based connections between Paddy and "the world". In this microcosm of community, smaller than a town and smaller still than a care home, the consideration of format, aim, and context were still active. In some senses, it was even more important to find ways of creating community, diversity of experience, and a creative life, when Paddy's reach was otherwise so limited. We took every emergent musical opportunity we could, to both optimize his rehabilitative potential and expand his social experience. These came to include filmmaking, graphic scores, composition, recording and programming, family jamming sessions, daily vocal exercises, and visits from local musical friends. Paddy even contributed to the Scrap Metal Project, albeit from afar, by helping to build a theremin from an enormous metal teapot, played during the concert by another group member. CoMT offered an approach that could meet Paddy as a patient, as a client, and then also for some time later, even as a home-based college student.

Multiple Values

From the early days of Paddy's recovery, music therapy came in diverse formats and activities, with varying aims, connecting him with different people, which then created multiple types of information and knowledge. Along with that multiplicity of practice and discourse came a multiplicity of value. The way we account for music therapy in a medical setting is different from how we might report it four years later in the client's own home. When that person then begins to re-enrol in their former college music course, their musical experiences start to count for something quite different again.

Does anything remain the same? One constant is music's ability to manifest a person. Our starting challenge, *"Show me what my son can still do"*, had successfully allowed us to manifest Paddy and show him in a different light, through his contextual connection with me and others through music. Now, however, the question had changed. The impulse had started to come from Paddy, not only from other people. Now he himself was asking the question, but in a new form. Now, he was saying, *"Let me show you what I can do"*. What he could do kept changing! Within this changing frame, not only of assessment and reporting but now also of enabling and of advocacy, the value of CoMT appears multimodal. This approach is of value within a medical or functional frame, but that frame is just one context amongst many. CoMT differs from much music therapy theory because it is formulated explicitly within a social and political framework. That framework recognizes that every context is constructed of a particular set of discourses. In order to communicate the value of Paddy's changing musical journey, I had to identify in which context of discourses I was communicating and learn the language.

"Evaluation" in Music Therapy

Within music therapy, the term "evaluation" can refer to a number of related processes and meanings (Tsiris, Pavlicevic, & Farrant, 2014). These meanings are often interlinked, such as when evaluation and assessment involve application of similar or identical processes; when evaluation processes carried out by observers also incorporate formal reflection by the music therapist; or when an evaluation process is framed and published as a research project. The purpose of this section is not to give a full account of how evaluation has grown to have these numerous applications, but instead to set out the emergent trends in this topic area related to CoMT.

Character and Scope of Evaluation

Assessment and Evaluation

The "consensus" characterization of evaluation in music therapy can refer to a number of interrelated knowledge practices concerning the status and progress of participants engaged in music therapy processes. This characterization of evaluation assumes that music therapy is a process that is predictable, treatment-based, sequential, and one in which a client's experience can be represented in terms that can be objectively measured and compared. By contrast, Ansdell (1995), for example, suggests that music therapy can also be a process that is not predictable or treatment-based, that is subjective and not easily represented in terms that use measurement. Rather than measuring effectiveness, evaluation might also be a process of charting development, or in Shoemark's terms, of "mapping progress" (2008). This approach to practice is articulated widely in music therapy literature, yet is reflected neither in the professional Standards of Proficiency, nor in the values that inform research databases such as the Cochrane Library.

The character and scope of CoMT imply an orientation toward, and impact on, a wider range of domains than standard evaluation traditionally has included (Ansdell, 2002; Curtis & Vaillancourt, 2012; Rolvsjord, 2006; Stige, 2002; Vaillancourt, 2012). It is not only in a broader approach to the possible types of impact that CoMT presents a challenge to standard notions of evaluation. It is also in the potential range of interested parties, participating agencies, and stakeholders who may require or read evaluation accounts. Curtis (2011) outlines a collaborative project designed to increase palliative care patient access to music therapy services by tapping into multiple university-community resources. These included resources of an undergraduate university music therapy program, of a professional symphony orchestra, and of funding available for university-community partnerships. Grocke et al. (2008) note that psychiatric care in Australia has shifted to community-based care, so that contemporary music therapy practice for the severely mentally ill has been reappraised alongside the principles of the recovery model. Ng (2011) asks if music therapy can be an answer to the "Terrorist Question". The possibility is raised in CoMT that social care agencies, cultural bodies, and whole communities are equally as likely to be participants as individuals.

Evaluating Art?

Another trend typically associated with CoMT practice is the foregrounding of artistic work as an end in itself. Shoshensky (2011) explores public creative expression as an intervention of CoMT for adult clients with long-term disabilities accessing supportive services such as post-acute rehabilitation, day treatment, and residential programs. He examines the issues involved in assisting clients in moving outside of traditional therapy settings and into the wider social contexts typically involved in music.

Shoshensky's work raises important challenges to the processes of evaluation, including the question of timing of evaluation, choice of outcome measures, and linking subjective value in artistic work with general notions of therapeutic effectiveness. This is also taken up to some extent in Turry (2005), where it is explored in relation to psychodynamic theory. It demonstrates not only that CoMT leads evaluation into broader interest groups or participants, but also that it is a likely site in which alternative value systems, such as artistic values, might take priority.

Methods of Evaluation

Purpose and Authorship

Within the music therapy profession, there is a broad range of evaluation and assessment tools, each of which is a response to different circumstances, expectations, and requirements. Bruscia, for example, writes:

> Procedures for conducting evaluations may include log reviews, team meetings, periodic narrative reports, systematic observations, a readministration of assessment procedures, and/or direct client feedback. Evaluation records may be in the form of narratives, data reports, or checklists. (1987, p. 15)

In recent literature, the range of evaluation tools in music therapy has proliferated. The trend in published reports is toward evaluation approaches or methods that are specific to diagnosis, social setting, or music therapy approach, but that are also based on general principles that carry validity or transferable meaning. Within this trend, it is common to find evaluation represented in the form of diagnosis-specific tools, increasingly designed for use within clinical specialisms in music therapy profession. For example, Carpente (2013) devised the Individual Music-Centered Assessment Profile for people living with neurodevelopmental disorders. This profile offers three scales, charting a Musical Emotional Assessment Rating, a Musical Cognitive/Perception Scale, and a Musical Responsiveness Scale. It is notable for the musical perspective that informs the whole profile.

In contrast, Baxter et al. (2007) produced the Individualized Music Therapy Assessment Profile (IMTAP). The profile aims to have general music therapy application and is a good example of the current trend in evaluation methods, dividing client presentation into ten "domains". In this profile, "Musicality" is considered its own domain, along with categories such as "Gross Motor" and "Cognitive". This model of assessment and evaluation is based on preplanned sessions, within which the music therapist will prejudge the areas for exploration and the musical structures to be used. Magee (2007a, 2007b) also presents a tool for assessing and evaluating client responses across a range of domains, within a music therapy setting with patients who are diagnosed as being in low awareness states. Her music therapy assessment tool for low awareness states (MATLAS) contains fourteen items that rate behavioural responses across a number of functional domains. Wosch and Wigram (2007) also give examples of recent assessment and evaluation methods produced predominantly from within a broad, individualist, objective approach. Whilst the stated focus of their work is on "microanalysis", the relevance here is that much of the microanalysis is presented as a technique associated with the process of evaluation. Each method synthesises a different perspective or theoretical foundation, articulated so that it might be a useful clinical tool:

> The authors have attempted to establish some simple, step-by-step (or stage-by-stage) procedures to guide clinicians, students, and researchers through the model that has been presented in order for it to become a functional, clinical model of analysis. (p. 299)

Recent examples of evaluation models developed by practitioners for specific clinical applications also include Abromeit (2003), Botello and Krout (2008), Chlan and Heiderscheit (2009), Dalton and Krout (2005), Daveson (2010), Hilliard (2001), Langhan (2009), Munk-Madsen (2001), Register and Hilliard (2008), Snow and D'Amico (2009), and Walworth (2007).

In contrast with the proliferation of individualised methods of music therapy evaluation, tools and methods seeking to reflect an alternative communal perspective are less numerous. Historically, they have included Ansdell (1991), Gilroy & Lee (1995), Nordoff and Robbins (1977), Pavlicevic (1997), Ruud (1998), and Stige (2002). Common amongst these methods is an approach that formulates the client and music in a psychosocial theoretical perspective. One method significantly associated with psychosocial evaluation approaches is self-report, discussed in Beard (2012), Chaffin and Imreh (2001), Nayak et al. (2000), Ulrich et al. (2007), and Wheeler et al. (2003). Without necessarily referencing CoMT, the psychosocial perspective has grown toward articulating a perspective on the person, music, and evaluation criteria that is different from the perspective inherent to individualist treatment models. This development raises questions about the status of knowledge generated by evaluation and the value of that knowledge in standard professional evaluation.

Tracking Wider Impact

From its earliest publications, CoMT has posed a challenge in relation to tools or methods of evaluation. This challenge has been connected to the wider range of impact generated by its practices. Tyson (1973) considered that CoMT represents an important developmental breakthrough, posing stimulating challenges and affording new opportunities for growth and service. More recently, the use of social science methodology has become associated with CoMT evaluation. For example, Snow et al. (2008) describe an innovative form of interdisciplinary research integrating social science and creative arts therapies methodologies. CoMT also creates a framework where practitioners feel able to bring a vast range of methodologies, in terms of both clinical practice and evaluation. Scheiby (2002), for instance, describes what she calls a 40-minute "CoMT" session with 48 participants that she evaluates through the lens of Analytical Music Therapy. It is not so much that CoMT requires one alternative method to individualist approaches, but instead that it opens up multiple possibilities.

Those possibilities are characterized by reflexivity and collaboration. Stige and Aarø (2012) note that the procedural requirements for CoMT often vary because practice often takes place in systems that have less formal expectations. Citing Vaillancourt (2009), they observe that "it is important for evaluation to be integrated into working processes, whether or not there is a system that formally calls for evaluation reports" (p. 222). They also note that evaluation in CoMT can become a more collaborative process than it is in standard systems.

What many systems of evaluation already point to is that music therapy impacts upon aspects of public health and secondary prevention, along with the primary focus of treatment or practice. This can be seen in fields as widespread as stroke rehabilitation (Tamplin et al., 2013), pulmonary disease (Azoulay, 2009; Griggs-Drane, 2009), coronary heart disease (Hanser and Mandel, 2014; Leist, 2011; Mandel et al., 2007), Alzheimer's disease (Harris and Caporella, 2014), child welfare (Krüger and Stige, 2015), substance misuse (Baker et al., 2012; Gardstrom et al., 2013; Mays et al., 2008; Silverman, 2011b, 2011c, 2012, 2015), rehabilitation of ex-offenders (Tuastad and O'Grady, 2013; Tuastad and Stige, 2015), mental illness (Iliya, 2011; Solli et al., 2013) and in the creation or use of social capital (Hussey et al., 2006; Procter, 2011). As a profession we are alert to the applications of music therapy both for localised functional change and also in relation to longitudinal impact upon public health. One challenge for evaluation is how to meet those twin agendas of accounting for causal functional change and for social or longterm impact in the realm of health promotion and wellbeing. It is possible that future CoMT evaluation strategies might help meet this challenge.

Objectivity and Validity

One area that would have to be addressed in relation to those twin agendas is the status of knowledge created in individualist and alternative evaluation methodologies. More specifically, there is an inherent scepticism in CoMT regarding objectivity and positivist research approaches. A concern about the status of knowledge reported in evaluations has become a significant trend in standard music therapy evaluation. Often this trend is formulated as a polarity between objectivist and constructivist paradigms. For example, O'Callaghan (2009a) argues that neither objectivist nor constructivist research will be able to capture an absolute "truth" about music therapy's effectiveness. See also Stige (2001), on objectivism and relativism. Within this debate, the concern is that nonstandard evaluation, prioritizing local or situated knowledge, might compromise professional credibility.

Another indication of the concern amongst the research community around standardization is the question of correlation and inter-rater agreement. Music therapists reportedly do not readily use the many published music therapy assessment tools available to them (Loewy, 1995). Jacobson (2009) wrote that the time has come for music therapists to conduct correlation studies to validate their assessment tools, including correlation with normative samples and/or psychological tests, even though it may take decades of research.

Inter-rater agreement is explored in Mahoney (2010), in relation to an evaluation scale designed by Nordoff and Robbins. Lane-Brown and Tate (2009) assess the efficacy of nonpharmacological treatments for apathy following four types of acquired brain impairment (traumatic brain injury, dementia, cerebrovascular accident, encephalitis). Their findings suggest a need for more rigorous treatment studies for apathy, particularly within the milder ranges of impairment. The authors argue that employing a standardised outcome measure specific to apathy would greatly enhance comparison amongst treatments. With similar concerns, Robb et al. (2011) explore the transparency and specificity of reporting music-based interventions. It is notable that reporting is here raised as an important aspect of the evaluation process.

Within CoMT, collaboration features as a significant trend reflecting a communal approach evaluation. This contrasts with the desire within more individualist perspectives for inter-rater agreement or objectivity. For O'Kelly and Koffman (2007), broad music therapy practice is an appropriate therapeutic intervention for meeting the holistic needs of palliative care service users. The authors suggest that more understanding and integration of music therapy could be encouraged with collaborative work, educational workshops, and the utilization of environmentally focused techniques.

A collaborative approach also features in Jampel (2011), who seeks to make the knowledge practices of evaluation more collaborative in his account of CoMT in a mental health setting. Whilst approaching his practice from a music psychotherapy perspective, he seeks to find ways of understanding performance that allow the music therapist to "describe, assess, analyze, and evaluate the components of what is happening both over time and in the moment" (2011, retrieved online). Jampel also raises the possibility that methods of evaluation respond to broadening methods of music therapy, suggesting that the practice outlined in Ansdell (2005), for example, necessitates a reframing of evaluative strategies. This is also raised in Oddy (2005).

The proliferation of evaluation tools and the debate around the status of knowledge in music therapy suggests that the notion of generalisability is problematic. There is a clear trend toward tools with common practical application, yet also an interest in maintaining the local and personal. This discrepancy may relate to the many purposes and applications of evaluation in practice. Nonetheless, studies predominantly reflect an individualist stance.

Strategic Uses of Evaluation

Diagnosis

Evaluation is often produced for specific strategic purposes, beyond the practice of professional reflexivity and reporting. A recent trend in music therapy evaluation concerns how it can play a role in diagnostic and clinical assessment. Music therapy assessment and evaluation can identify aspects of autism in children, for example, detailing limitations as well as strengths and potential. Wigram (2007) suggests that evaluation can help identify diagnosis, needs, and potentials and set expectations for what may be achieved through intervention. There is a role for music therapy evaluation in providing information for other, more general, assessment processes, such as in Scalenghe and Murphy (2000), who provide specific suggestions for music therapy assessments that will meet managed care requirements.

Diagnosis is based in a political relationship of expert to client. Whilst this is commensurate with a medical or clinical model of music therapy and thus with the individualist "standard" approach, it does not fit so easily with a communal model in which there may be no presumption of an expert–client dyad. In some examples of CoMT, music is understood to be a resource that is shared collaboratively. In such instances, the notion of diagnosis would be unhelpful.

The collaborative character of CoMT evaluation creates an opportunity for it to have wider applications than standard medical or individualist approaches. Stige and Aarø (2012) suggest that evaluation itself can be of strategic importance for its participants:

> Several characteristics of evaluation in action research are relevant for CoMT, such as evaluation through collective discussion and reflection, evaluation as mutual empowerment, evaluation as a continuous or cyclical process, and evaluation informed by an extended epistemology. (p. 222)

The authors suggest that inclusion of stakeholders is "crucial" (p. 223) in CoMT. In Oosthuizen, Fouché, and Torrance (2007), the application of collaborative work between music therapists and community musicians is explored in the context of the development of a South African CoMT project.

Funding and Professional Status

Favourable evidence can be influential in gaining funding for music therapy services. Edwards (2011) describes how evaluations of a "Sing & Grow" programme have been critical for obtaining significant funding for the expansion of the programme across Australia. See also Abad and Williams (2007). Phillips-Salimi et al. (2011) provide a model for development and evaluation of a "data collection integrity monitoring plan" for behavioural interventions that may be adapted by investigators and may be useful to funding agencies and grant application reviewers in evaluating proposals.

Within either approach, evaluation is also critical for establishing professional credibility. Ahn and Ashida (2012) suggest that gaps exist in music therapy evaluation, preventing music therapy from being considered part of evidence-based medicine or even a clinical expertise. They suggest that successful establishment of its efficacy will enable further research to understand how inexpensive and safe music therapy programs may be disseminated in the community. Mongrain and Trambakoulos (2007) justify their study by how it validated a new musical mood induction procedure. Professional considerations in evaluation are discussed further by Procter (2006) and Wilhelm (2004). Evaluation can also be important in generating critical mass, as highlighted by Mrázová and Celec (2010), and to inform other professionals about music therapy processes, as noted by Hulme et al. (2010) and Maue-Johnson and Tanguay (2006).

Powell (2006) presents an example of how CoMT practice can be targeted both toward professional accountability and to promote a continuation of the practice through funding or management support. In some examples, specific social and public health problems are identified as possible areas of attention for music therapy, as with Gilbertson (2008), who asks what music therapy can do to combat road traffic accidents. The trend in the CoMT approach is for evaluation to take a broader view of what might be achieved through practice, and also through the reporting of that practice.

These applications of evaluation suggest that evaluation has a performative element, in the sense that it is a process with an agenda relating to professional, economic, or political outcomes in addition to its practical purposes. This element seems common within both "standard" and CoMT literature.

Music Therapy Evaluation Is Performative

In music therapy, "evaluation" is a term without fixed meaning and a process without fixed parameters, yet it is also a requirement that is acknowledged commonly, both within the music therapy profession and within the research field. Methods of evaluation range from qualitative self-reports, journals, and observation to large, randomized, controlled trials. Evaluation appears to take place during music therapy, immediately after, and also in follow-up. Other examples of evaluation are time-controlled experimental situations. Each example of timing might suggest a different theoretical orientation. There is also a wide variation of effects and outcomes. These include measurable physical effects on a gross/fine motor level in terms of cell growth and on a chemical level, observed social interaction on intimate and wide social scales, reports of improvement in quality of life, and inferred impact on aspects such as behaviour, cognitive ability, and self-image.

The main problematic factor is that CoMT presents multiple benefits or applications, creating an array of evaluation or research possibilities, with many consequent methodological considerations. Music therapy evaluation has numerous purposes, and can be reported effectively, or not, according to those purposes. The evaluation materials that then emerge from music therapy practice could be understood as a form of performance: a transmission of knowledge derived from experience, driven not only by specialist music therapy interests but also by other interests such as research agendas, workplace demands, funding, or wider cultural forces. I would argue that more work is required to acknowledge this performance, not to "solve" a supposed problem with evaluation, but to articulate aspects of the ecology that produces and transmits it.

Matrix Diagram of Evaluation

Functional Interaction Matrix Assessment (*fi*-ma)

One possible step in that direction is to build an evaluation matrix based on the hybrid principles of function and interaction. The solution shared here is one possible method. The anticipated primary user would be a music therapist working in a setting where both lasting functional change and new social or artistic interactions are expected outcomes of practice. Within the terms of CoMT, it could be assumed that settings of this type may present both scheduled and spontaneous music therapy sessions; musical encounters may be planned and regular, but they may also be brief or circumstantial or occur in passing.

In CoMT, assessment and evaluation are not performed on the basis that music is "applied" to a person regardless of their context, after which the "outcome" of the music is measured. They are also not necessarily based on the idea of preplanned sessions. This perspective may consider the person's functional interaction to be continually reformed and manifest in the moment by the music, and to be affected by the setting or format in which they are playing. It may even seek alternative modes of representation to verbal or numeric allusions to objectivity.

This means that assessment would primarily describe how the person (or indeed their social group or community) is manifest whilst music is happening, rather than propose to measure the result of their playing; that assessment over time might uncover different aspects and shades of a person, group, or community rather than evidence incremental improvement; and that the questions that surround the assessment will focus on elements such as the daily life, family or carer relations, and preferred formats of practice as well as the achievement of functional goals. It is also assumed that sessions or musical encounters may have been spontaneous and highly improvised in session structure as well as in musical material.

It is also possible that this sort of assessment and evaluation could be carried out collaboratively, both with participants themselves and with other stakeholders such as carers and family members. This would make session reviews powerful methods of reflection and goal-setting. To reflect this, space is left to record both who is making the assessment and who is the subject of the assessment: an individual, a group, or a community.

Assessment Methodology

The *fi*-ma is an observational tool designed to focus on describing in detail how a person, group, or community is active when making music. In particular, it seeks to offer qualitative assessment and communication using a structured method. It is formulated as a working document to enable practitioners and participants to think more widely about service delivery, review, and design.

The grid presented here is the starting point for an in-depth observational method, presenting musicality as it emerges over time. That time span could be a short moment within one session or a period of ten weeks or even longer, depending on the focus of the assessment and evaluation. This assessment can, if necessary, provide a numeric composite score to denote level of functional interaction, but it can also act more descriptively as a prompt for collaborative discussion.

The formative principles of this tool are:

- Everyone has the potential to respond to music

- Music therapy can be understood in terms of functional development
- Music therapy occurs when function is performed through interaction
- Musicality can be profiled by functional interaction
- Performance in music therapy cannot be preplanned
- Assessment is a still image of being in motion
- In music, the individual and communal are manifest together

These principles suggest that whilst the usual focus of assessment will be one person, identifiably a "client" or person with a specific diagnosis, there may be situations in which the "person" is assessed as part of a group or where the "person" is indeed a whole community itself. In this way, the *fi*-ma tool should be able to apply to a flexible definition of the person and reflect change in any system.

Assessment Method

As is common amongst assessment and evaluation tools, *fi*-ma is based on the assessor's judgment in observing activity. This judgement is systematized to a degree by setting out ten dimensions of activity and three subskills that relate to each dimension. In the assessment grid shown below, the assessor(s) would divide the time period in question into ten equal time segments. Their reflective process would record where the dimensions of the client/group or community manifest in low/mid/high activity. The completed assessment grid provides a graphic representation of musical activity across time, which can easily be converted into a numeric rating if required. The graphic representation is organized in a grid-matrix format. The emergent impression from the completed matrix provides a view not only of a static functional level, but also of a dynamic change in musical interaction over the session.

"Function" and "Interaction"

The *fi*-ma is designed to look and feel like a standard assessment and evaluation profiling tool. It can provide information about "functional" change, and it can also lead to questions and choices about "interactive" experience. For instance, the assessor(s) would use the same assessment framework whether the person was in an individual session with functional goals like PJ or Paddy or in a choral project like Caryl; what would change is the relative value of functional goals and cultural interaction, which would affect the range of activity observed. Consequently, the interpretation of the analysis might differ in focus, vocabulary, or application, and the written descriptions of the goals and activities themselves would inform the reader of the work's details.

In another example, the focus on emotional activity would have been recorded differently in PJ's early individual sessions than in her later public workshops, because of the social situation. This would have been a factor in the choice of session format initially, based on the priority of that dimension of the work and her wider needs and interests. However, it would still be possible to assess the issue of emotional flexibility in a larger setting, because that dimension is still, of course, active and relevant.

The basic understanding of *fi*-ma is that the musical benefit in a given situation is seen in the interplay between a person or group's many active functions, in the interactive use of those functions, and in how those are experienced in real-life settings. This challenge to standard modes of assessment and evaluation has led to a grid-matrix formation that presents musicality by juxtaposing multidimensional functional interaction against time.

Dimensions

The *fi*-ma is organized under the ten dimensions discussed on p.87. Those dimensions are:

- Fine Motor
- Gross Motor
- Oral Motor
- Sensory
- Attention
- Expression
- Social
- Emotional
- Cognitive
- Creative

The profile of a person's musicality is illustrated by how these dimensions reconfigure over time.

Subskills

Each dimension of activity is divided for assessment into three subskills. Those skills are defined below. It might be that part of a collaborative assessment and evaluation process would be to redefine these subskills to include more specific experiences into the assessment.

Dimension	Subskills
Fine Motor	Grip
	Point/press
	Pluck
Gross Motor	Reach
	Beat (including play piano)
	Dance
Oral Motor	Mouth
	Make vocal sounds
	Speak/sing
Sensory	Gaze in direction of sound/speech
	Tolerate or initiate touch
	Engage via more than one sense
Attention	Hold concentration
	Engage in activity
	Show intention to be present
Expression	Use expressive components
	Use opportunities for expression
	Flexible use of expressive components
Social	Tolerate interpersonal situations
	Show confidence and purpose in being with others
	Work as an equal partner (in time, effort, or musical content)
Emotional	Tolerate own emotional presence
	Maintain stable emotional state
	Understand emotional needs in others
Cognition	React to stimuli
	Follow tasks
	Process complex tasks
Creativity	Respond with new ideas
	Change with circumstances
	Collaborate

Fig. 7: Music therapy subskills

Where Is Music?

There is a question within music therapy assessment and evaluation of where and how music is represented. In some models, musicality is a separate domain of analysis. In others, it is a basic assumption of the practice and thus the analysis itself. In *fi*-ma, music is assumed to be the unique organization of functional interaction, across all the dimensions of personhood. It is not treated as a separate category. Instead, *fi*-ma attempts to provide a visual impression not only of the individual functional level of a person, group, or community, but also of their overall musical portrait as it changes over time.

Implications For Theory

This theory section considers the implications of emergence and performativity for CoMT evaluation. It will touch briefly on the question of simultaneity in assessment and treatment, the performativity of personhood and music, the politics of evaluation language, and on some of the questions around procedure, collaboration, ethics, and impact.

Simultaneity

The most common schema for understanding the character and scope of music therapy evaluation is the comparative, causal characterisation associated with Bruscia (1987). This supposes that a music therapist can collect and analyse initial information, implement an effective treatment programme, and then review that by evaluating client progress in relation to the treatment. That schema is essentially sequential and may take place over a period of weeks or months.

CoMT often entails musical situations in which the method and moment of "assessment" are simultaneously the manifestation of the method and moment of "treatment". This style of practice involves an integral stance of continual reflexive evaluation and often informal reporting, rather than a stage of formal reporting. Where formal reporting does occur, it may not contain information that provides causal links between treatment and outcomes.

Functional Interaction Musical Assessment (*fi*-ma)
Assessment Grid

Date	Client/Group/Community									
Prepared by										
	1	**2**	**3**	**4**	**5**	**6**	**7**	**8**	**9**	**10**
Fine motor (F)										
Gross motor (G)										
Oral motor (O)										
Sensory (Se)										
Attention (A)										
Expression (Ex)										
Social skills (So)										
Emotional (Em)										
Cognition (Co)										
Creativity (Cr)										

Main areas of activity	

Key: [blank] (low/minimal: 0) / (mid: 0.5) / (high: 1)

Fig. 8: Assessment grid

Performing Person, Performing Music

CoMT not only has the potential to impact numerously upon individual people, but also it can impact upon other "persons", too. "Persons" such as companies, charities, lobbying groups, or social movements may also be incorporated into the range of potential benefit offered by CoMT, expanding upon previous theoretical work on this by Bruscia (1998) and Stige (2002), for example. This points to the need for a more detailed concept of musical communicativeness from an organizational perspective, suggesting that active musical partnership may be a phenomenon that can be performed not only between individuals in dyads or groups, but also across organizations, transversally.

This idea would build on the notion expressed by Bruscia (1998, p. 229) that CoMT expands and complexifies the definition of "the client". It also adds to the ongoing clarifications throughout Stige et al. (2010) regarding the differences between "client", "participant", and "musician". It suggests first that those who benefit from CoMT can be individuals with stated "needs", but also that they can be individuals without a needs-based association (such as family members or supporters), groups of people with specific and/or unclear membership, and, in fact, any institutional, social, or cultural entity or interest.

In CoMT, the definition of "client" (a person with a specific professional relationship to the therapist, defined by duty of care), in contrast with participant, or beneficiary, is sometimes unclear. Even insofar as an individual is specifically referred through medical channels, in some cases, family members or other social groupings will warrant duty of care or will manifest other types of client attributes. This is further complicated by the tendency of practitioners in CoMT to look beyond the functional/instrumental aspects of practice even when working with people who have stated clinical or psychosocial needs. On an individual level, CoMT assumes that an individual is different according to the mode of musical experience they are in. Those individuals and the organizations around them may alter further according to how they are part of musical experience. They are performing constantly. The exploration of performance via discourse has thrown new light on what it might then mean to speak of a "performing person".

An individual may indeed be understood and thus "performed" differently by varying contexts, according to the types of information or knowledge generated by and about them. This may well be affected by how they are in music— whether they are highly passive recipients or producing musical events in what would ordinarily be termed "performance" situations. An individual is performed continuously by the network they are in at any moment. Significant aspects of how a person is in a given context are created by the context itself, contributing to how the person is "performed" in that moment.

The same may be suggested of the organization itself; a company or charity performs its own personhood and that of those it connects with. The impact of CoMT within that personhood may be significant. Perhaps there is further exploration to be done in uncovering aspects of how an organization is integrated or made coherent via musical processes, and how CoMT is particularly placed to contribute and inform those processes.

The notion of the "performing person" is not necessarily limited to an individual moment of witnessed music-making. CoMT tends to assume that aspects of musicality, sound, meaning-making, and presence are woven into organizational structures, too. A decentred approach to music, or "music-as-mileu" (Stige & Aarø, 2012, p. 119), can help in understanding how organizations and systems "music". It may therefore be significant to record and observe the many processes around the moment of witnessed music-making. Those paramusical activities of creating ideas, seeing opportunities, planning events, and involving participants in complex sociocultural situations may be highly relevant for understanding the performed value of music in CoMT.

Politics of Evaluation Language

In CoMT, a further consideration emerges, which is that terms such as "treatment", and even "effectiveness", can appear politically charged. Even where an activity is planned, monitored, and recorded, it may not have been within a frame that views it as "treatment" of specific needs, with an outcome that demonstrates "effectiveness". CoMT practice may be framed in terms of responding to social situations or emerging out of particular conditions. In such circumstances, the evaluation will reflect the values and vocabulary of that frame (and thus may chart impact rather than provide evidence of effectiveness). Whilst this may be viewed purely as a technical problem of language, the technicalities of language perform political realities for those participating in the discourse (see Stige, 2014).

Those political realities have power implications, as the act of framing a set of interests within discourse has the opposite effect, too: of excluding, or "othering" another set of interests. As Law and Mol (2002) write, "… this implies the need for endless determinations about the location of the boundary between what is real and to be made manifest on the one hand, and what is to be Othered on the other" (p. 96). The process of creating an evaluation narrative within CoMT may therefore be enhanced by paying more attention to which discourses are "louder" at a given moment and which are "drowned out" by more powerful voices.

CoMT is based in the notion that practice is context-led and that contexts change. The implication of this is that evaluations are valid only for one location, at one time, and in that sense, they perform the particularities of the participants in that moment. The challenge for CoMT is to transpose the information generated from that immediate performance into information that satisfies the formal requirements of its professional standards and the varied discourses of its stakeholders, without contributing to the silencing of the weakest voices.

This is not to suggest that the idea that evaluation is performative implies that it is a misrepresentation. The performance of evaluation could instead be thought of as a faithful act of transposition. This notion echoes Ansdell's (1996) Music Therapist's Dilemma, concerning the act of putting musical experience into language. CoMT can perform evaluation both by creating (and re-creating) the presence of musical experience and by representing information about the experience, and can do so in a language that can be received effectively and appropriately by its audience. In this, it has much to offer the music therapy profession in general, by suggesting how the so-called problems of evaluating music therapy may instead usefully illuminate some of its key, if under-acknowledged, features.

Procedure and Content

Stige and Aarø (2012) note that procedural requirements for CoMT evaluation vary because practice often occurs in settings with varying levels of formality in their expectations. This is also seen in Vaillancourt (2009) in relation to the demands of evidencing beneficial change in relation to highly collaborative fields such as social justice. The practitioner will also have their own way of processing the phenomena of their work. This generates a spectrum of formality for the music therapist in the evaluation of their professional practice. This spectrum is not necessarily problematic, if reporting strategies become more adept at promoting its inherent diversity. In some senses, if evaluation remains difficult to assimilate into information systems, it could be evidence that it is still performative and still creative.

Collaborative Strategies

There is great potential in combining the many discourses connected to CoMT in more collaborative evaluation strategies. A challenge remains in drawing together the possible collaborative formations to process CoMT evaluation effectively. Modern technology allows for innovative approaches to collaboration, via social media, digital storage of information, and the rise of cloud-based software systems. It might be that the "from the ground up" systems that underpin examples such as Wiki, Twitter, and Facebook might offer attractive solutions to the questions raised by evaluation of CoMT.

Inclusion and Ethics

It might be asked, however, whether there is an optimum limit to the scope of CoMT evaluation. Music is noted in the literature to have the potential to impact widely upon health and social care contexts (Ansdell & DeNora, 2012). There may be a point at which the political and ethical considerations involved in evaluation could curb the expansion of musical practice. It has been suggested in this study that the impact of musical experience can be felt remotely, both in space and time, via skilled broadcasting or publishing. It is already possible that recorded evidence of CoMT can be witnessed without the music therapist's knowledge and have an impact of which they remain unwaware. At what point does this challenge professional ethics and create an untenable politics of inclusion?

CoMT is based in a music-centred approach that proposes that all people *can* respond to music. Its ecological theoretical framework suggests that via the ripple effect and the paramusical processes of organizations, all people in a given context *do* respond, in some senses, to music. It may be a professional risk to let this develop into the notion that within the scope of CoMT, all people *should* be included in responding to music, whatever their status in the ecology.

Considerations for "Effective" Evaluation Strategies

It was also significant in the studies that certain methods of evaluation were observed to have more impact than others. It was noted that images, film, and recordings seemed especially potent in creating the feeling of the practice, whereas numeric data was important in representing professionalism and conforming to the requirements of governance. Thus the studies suggest that evaluation methods would perform value in an ecology differently according to the methods used and the intended audience.

The opinion of stakeholders, and a broader definition of clienthood and participation, also impact upon the question of evaluation methods. This may apply to other arts in health practices, too, as suggested in Daykin et al. (2011, 2012, 2013). The interests of some stakeholders may include more physiological change (such as hormonal or immune-system change), as well as social impact. It could be asked whether these are compatible criteria for evaluation. If so, it may be that a future evaluation pack might include online feedback options (not only for clients, but also for family, friends, and staff), text or Twitter addresses, space for photographs, and an oral swab for saliva tests. This then raises the question of who the person in CoMT is: How are they formulated, and when does that formulation change?

A significant issue for the field of evaluation methods in music therapy is the question of correlation studies or inter-rater agreement. The range of discourses addressed within music therapy evaluation is already broad, and there is no assurance of inter-rater agreement within those discourses. Indeed, within some discourses, the concept may not even apply. Whilst correlation may be one approach to navigating this diversity, another approach involving the assemblage of epistemologies could create composite evaluation reports. This would involve an exploration beyond current examples of mixed-methods research, engaging more thoroughly with what differing epistemologies might offer each other. Evaluation methods and discourses may not need to match; they may help by fitting together. New technologies and social media may equally apply to general music therapy evaluation. Where music therapy is practiced within an individualist frame, it must still be communicated to an increasingly diverse audience. It is possible that the systems that support from-the-ground-up social technologies might assist in the correlation proposed above.

If the processes of music can apply variously to individuals and large organizations, it follows that the potential for evaluation criteria also proliferates. CoMT broadens music's impact beyond physiological symptoms and health-promotion strategies (as discussed by Ansdell & Meehan, 2010, and Ruud, 2007, for example) and points even to its applications in the home, the workplace, and towns and cities.

It may be that in some contexts even the commercial and marketing value of practice is a relevant discourse for evaluation. Commercial and marketing value has been discussed in relation to general music therapy literature (Romo & Gifford, 2007, for example), but it may be that CoMT is especially open to appropriation by these discourses, as it is often more easily witnessed and social in scope (Pavlicevic & Fouché, 2014). Two significant implications may arise from this in relation to the epistemologies that are required in order to process such values, and possible professional questions regarding the integrity and ethics of a focus on commerce and marketing.

Toward "FACETs"

Perhaps more than any other, the topic of evaluation illuminates for us the many "FACETs" of CoMT and the need for an integrated matrix approach to it. This is indeed a multifaceted approach, involving a multiplicity of Formats, Aims, Context, and Evaluation. Theory has also been shown, as a thread throughout this book, to be an important "FACET" of CoMT. An understanding of ecological perspectives, emergence, the rhizome, and performativity is essential for the further understanding of how we discover what people can do in CoMT.

Chapter 8

CONCLUSION

Summary

"FACETs" of CoMT

By now, you may be thinking, *"CoMT is not so much a thing you do, nor is it especially a way of doing it either. It's a way of thinking"*. You may be near the mark. The desire of most authors to avoid definitions, and instead point to its key features, is in some ways an example of emergent thinking. Cold comfort in some respects for the practitioner, but a sort of liberation, too. All the same, the features by which we can recognize CoMT are located within its ecological perspective, tending to a decentred approach to personhood, music, and need. These elements are seen as emergent manifestations of a widespread and ever-changing psychosocial ecology. I suggested here that knowledge about how this ecology works can be formalised sufficiently using a matrix with nonhierarchical, nonlinear structures. What we are likely to be addressing through this matrix are questions concerning the main "FACETs" of CoMT: Formats, Aims, Context, Evaluation, and Theory. Two main concepts have become necessary for considering these "FACETs": emergence and performativity. The section below summarises these "FACETs" and main concepts. It goes on to discuss some of the implications of this approach.

Formats

I used the term "format", in line with Pavlicevic and Ansdell (2004), to denote a way of describing a music therapy encounter. It relates, literally, to the formal construction of our moments of connection. In this book, I have described individual improvisational formats, 1:1 tuition and composition, small groups, workshops, bands, concerts, trips, rehearsals, joint sessions, family times, community singing times, corporate events, community arts projects, and college courses. Writing in another time, or another place, I would have been describing a different set of formats.

Aims

When choosing a format of practice, the prime consideration is "what for?" Sometimes the format and aim of practice will emerge both naturally and simultaneously. At others, we have to think in what looks like a linear way. Certainly, a linear narrative is important when reporting professionally, so that the multiplicity of practice can be translated into the credible language of aims and outcomes. This is performative in two ways: first, in that it is an emergent manifestation of that translation, and produced by it, and second, in that it then creates new political realities such as professional status or increased awareness around you.

Context

The multiple character of formats and aims in CoMT generates a widely dispersed range of interested parties, stakeholders, values, and modes of communication. These produce a large list of discourses, threading through and around your practice. In this book, I described the matrix of discourses in a large care home company, setting out 17 discourses that could have been active in co-constructing that context. The professional music therapy discourse is one of those, and many choices may come from that line, but it is not the only discourse out there, and it will be affected by the many others that surround and connect with it. The context of CoMT is explicitly performative of what I would argue is a long list of practices and values.

Evaluation

The emergent formats, aims, and contextual elements in CoMT challenge us in making choices, documenting those choices, and evaluating the process. CoMT presents multiple beneficial outcomes or impacts, across a potentially wide range of stakeholders. Typically, knowledge practices around evaluation are both informal and formal, contained in diverse methods and concepts. I shared here a starting point for matrix thinking around evaluation. The *fi*-ma assessment grid uses the concept of functional interaction to define the activity of CoMT. The grid presents a matrix of personal dimensions over time. The person within the grid could be a named individual but could also be a group or community. The grid-matrix works on the basis that musicality is manifest in the organized activity of a person's many dimensions. This method presents an initial step in presenting and performing how that activity works.

Theory

The theory interwoven into these chapters employs a small number of important words. These include "manifest", "emerge", "complex", "multiple", and "performative". Whilst the last two decades have seen significant inroads into developing these concepts further, there remains a need for us to find new ways of talking about the simultaneous manifesting of the person, music, and context that is the hallmark of CoMT. I feel that this offers insight for music therapy and is still one of the main contributions that CoMT can make. It is possible that an enhanced concept of emergence and performativity in particular will be central parts of our theory in the coming years.

Emergence

Emergence is in some ways about how something comes from nothing. It is a very creative concept, concerning the way forms (such as neuronal configurations, swarms, cities, or indeed music) manifest out of their constituent parts. You might imagine it to be like a "Magic Eye" image, seemingly a mass of coloured elements until your focus shifts and out pops an elephant or a battleship. The sacred Sufi geometries give us emergence, too. At each level of magnification, another set of shapes and forms comes into being, each in relation to the last and to the next. Here, I have characterised formats of practice, knowledge, and contextual relationships all as emergent elements. The precise shape of these emergent elements is performative of their unique situation.

Performativity

What does it mean to suggest that an individual is performed by the network they are in at any moment? To think that significant aspects of how a person is in a given context are created by the context itself? The same may be asked of an organization itself, of a company or charity performing its own personhood, and of those with whom it connects. The impact of CoMT within that personhood may be significant. Perhaps there is further exploration to be done in uncovering aspects of how any organization (a brain, a body, a duo, a group, a hospital, a care company, or a culture) is integrated or made coherent via musical processes and how CoMT is placed to contribute and inform those processes.

Implications

Where would this exploration start? Those more recent theorists who have built upon Nietzsche, Hume, and Spinoza (Deleuze, Nancy), Hegel (Butler), and Kant (Bourdieu) offer an entry point that is less arbitrary than most. This line of enquiry would develop our understanding of the paradoxes inherent in CoMT and raised in this book. To find an integrative way of thinking about these paradoxes and not split them, I have followed the convention of Actor-network Theory (Latour, 2005) and presented them here in hybrid terms: the essential-contingent; the single-multiple; the material-semiotic; the intrinsic-instrumental; and the clinical-communal. These are paradoxes that typify CoMT and that are hotly current concerns within aesthetics, gender studies, ethnography, and critical studies. They have been the stuff of the mystics, poets, and teachers for far longer. I suspect that around Rumi's circle, along with his befuddled students, sit Oscar Wilde, John Cage, and many of our own muses and teachers, very probably laughing.

The Essential-Contingent

One of the main strands of CoMT thinking is that music is multifaceted and co-constructed. This view would say that music is "contingent" upon contextual interactions and conditions; music is not a "thing-in-itself", with no universals or essentials across time or territory. The problem is, of course, that whilst this makes a sort of theoretical sense and might feel intuitively right to many readers, our work is based on a belief that when I play music with you, we both feel something the same way. Whether we relate that to Vitality Affect, to entrainment in heart rate, or to shared prosody, pitch accuracy, or empathic intuition, music therapists base quite a lot of our professional assertions on the idea that within this contingent musical playing, we have shared something essential.

One journey we all might want to make together is toward ways of explaining how music can be somehow shared, yet also somehow unique to individuals. What, if anything, is essential in music? What, if anything, is contingent? Are they ineffably separate? Put another way, how do we approach subjectivity in CoMT? And is there a current thread already within philosophy that can frame this sort of question? Deleuze and Guattari provide a starting point, in which they use art (most commonly cinema, although sometimes music, too) as an example. Colebrook (2002) explains their enquiry in this way:

> Artists must constantly plunge back into the depths of experience in order to release the sensibilities from which actual experience is composed. Philosophers have to re-create concepts that give "consistency" to chaos; we have to constantly reopen thinking to the outside without allowing a fixed image of that outside to act as one more foundation. Philosophers create concepts that, far from functioning as grounds or points of agreement and recognition, allow us to think of the difference, discontinuity, and chaos which surrounds and passes through us. (pp. 77–78)

In this philosophical approach, music can be understood as a common ground of difference. It equips us to nurture difference, to celebrate each person's uniqueness, their chaotic becoming, but from a common point of "consistency". How we unpack this paradox within our own professional discourse is a question for further conversation.

The Single-Multiple

One device for exploring the essential-contingent question is what social theorists such as Latour, Woolgar, Law, Mol, and others have given us in their work on performativity and the multiple. How do we talk about music, if it is more than one thing (contingent) yet less than many (essential)? Law writes (2004):

> if we attend to practice, we tend to discover multiplicity, *but not pluralism.* For the absence of singularity does not imply that we live in a world composed of an indefinite number of different and disconnected bodies it does not imply that reality is fragmented. Instead it implies something much more complex. It implies that the

different realities *overlap and interfere with one another.*
Perhaps we should imagine that we are in a world of
fractional objects. A fractional object would be an object
that was more than one and less than many. (pp. 61–62;
italics in original)

This notion harks back to the consideration of the musical score earlier
in this text. A musician is always one *plus,* and surely a music therapist is,
too. We understand music as a process of unfolding, of leaning into the
future, and we understand people in therapy in the same way. What might
it add to our discourse if we were to explore the fractal, not in the sense
of incompleteness, but perhaps in the sense of being made complete in
having been met?

The Material-Semiotic

But how, who, and what do we meet in music? I have suggested that the
context in which we operate is co-constructed amongst a vast order, type,
and reach of elements. This simple act of playing music together is the
culmination of countless interactions that have been both material (cells,
bodies, hands, sticks, and drums connecting) and semiotic (thoughts,
words, languages, meaning, and understandings somehow commonly
held). Some of what we know about professional music therapy practices
comes out of these interactions with (apparently) inanimate objects. Think
for a moment about how a client's experience would differ if you were to
use a different therapy room, or if you dyed your hair, or if you brought
out a different drum. Materials matter. Think also, however, about how
you process those material realities back into the work: what you say, how
you read responses, how you mitigate against distraction or anxiety.
Language and discourse matter, too. In fact, the point I would suggest is
that in music therapy, they are not so different.

Again, my main interest would be in the ways of thinking that can
help us explore this as a hybrid. Aesthetics (e.g., Nancy, 2005; Rancière,
2007) as well as ANT (e.g., Mol, 2002; Latour & Woolgar, 1979; Law, 2004)
give us an enticing direction in approaching the fractal types of knowledge
produced by the interaction of materiality and language. These thoughts
would apply as much to a clinical RCT as they would to a Participatory
Action Research study and affect any practitioner, whether they shared
aims and objectives or not.

The Intrinsic-Instrumental

In 1890, following the publication of *The Picture of Dorian Gray,* an intrigued young fan wrote to its author, Oscar Wilde, and asked him to explain a now-famous line included in its preface. The line read, *"All art is quite useless".* Wilde responded with a letter which read:

> 16, TITE STREET,
> CHELSEA. S.W.
>
> My dear Sir
>
> Art is useless because its aim is simply to create a
> mood. It is not meant to instruct, or to influence
> action in any way. It is superbly sterile, and the note of
> its pleasure is sterility. If the contemplation of a work
> of art is followed by activity of any kind, the work is
> either of a very second-rate order, or the spectator has
> failed to realise the complete artistic impression.
>
> A work of art is useless as a flower is useless. A flower
> blossoms for its own joy. We gain a moment of joy by
> looking at it. That is all that is to be said about our
> relations to flowers. Of course, man may sell the
> flower, and so make it useful to him, but this has
> nothing to do with the flower. It is not part of its
> essence. It is accidental. It is a misuse. All this is I fear
> very obscure. But the subject is a long one.
>
> Truly yours,
>
> Oscar Wilde
>
> *(Manuscripts and Letters of Oscar Wilde, Courtesy of
> the Morgan Library and Museum, New York)*

The subject is indeed a long one. Little did Wilde anticipate the brows that would furrow in contemplation of intrinsic or instrumental value in music therapy, over a century later. Music therapy makes brilliant use of art's uselessness. This is not fanciful. The pure operation of aesthetic becoming is by definition free from necessity. It is not fixed to a single causation, nor is it linked to a single purpose. Aesthetic production between people, and in materials, is the emergence of fractal encounters that occur as flowers occur. Flowering is a very good word for it. All the same, the art and science of music therapy have found strikingly diverse applications for this flowering that are profoundly useful to many different people.

This great diversity, and wide application, is surely a strength, but also probably what made my consultant's question so hard to answer. What we do is always a balance of art's intrinsic property of flowering on the one hand and purposeful strategic use on the other. The relation between what I have called here "aiming" and "allowing" is very hard to put into words, and it changes moment-to-moment according to the processes involved in practice. This question of balance applies right across the spectrum, from clinically driven, medically informed music therapy to the most socially co-constructed, art-based community work.

The Clinical-Communal

What emerges now is this: The clinical and communal are in a complex relationship. What we call the "clinical" is contextually and socially produced, yet what we call the "communal" is professionally framed and often clinically evaluated. Although I have presented CoMT as an alternative to "individualist perspectives" in music therapy, it is not a clear opposition. It is another point of view that has emerged on the same field as those individualist, clinical approaches that I outlined earlier. CoMT would not have a point of view to offer if it hadn't emerged through the validating processes of a credible profession. And it is clear that community musicians outside the profession make great use of clinical music therapy research to justify and endorse their practice.

There is a valuable critique within CoMT of the associations of "clinical" language (e.g., Procter, 2002) that comes from an engagement with the empowerment and enabling often found within more politically oriented approaches. The term is used with widely different meanings, as too is the term "communal". Of course, these terms do carry meanings that can point in different directions. My closing thought, however, is that they at least mark out the same playing field, and for that reason, they remain in an important, albeit complex, relationship. As values within music therapy, they are part of the matrix that produces what, and how, we play.

An Answer

I suggested at the start of this book that many of us might have had a recrimination about what we "should have said" in response to a difficult music therapy question. My own big question was from my consultant-in-rehabilitation, who asked me what one of his patients could do and how I would work with him. So simple, yet so complex! In one respect, this book has intended to set out in long form my answer to that question. I am glad, on reflection, that I have had some time to think about it.

But what actually happened at the time? Some weeks after failing to really answer his question, I found myself running an open music therapy group in a large social area in the rehabilitation unit. Attending were seven patients (one joined by his wife), a health care assistant, and a nurse. The room was full of things: people, orchestral percussion, expectations, abandoned cups of tea, dining tables, magazines, splints, problems, walking frames, wheelchairs, and colourful handmade posters on the walls. The consultant walked by, presumably en route to a clinical appointment. He looked busy. Unable to speak, yet keen to be hostly, one patient gestured to the consultant as if to say, "Come and join us". The invitation was tentative, but it was a natural communal action of reaching beyond the boundaries of their limited daily clinical encounters. I spotted, then, with some relief, an opportunity to provide an answer. Pausing the fragile pulse for a moment, I offered the consultant the smallest, most delicate instrument I had at hand, made a space for him amongst his patients, and we all carried on playing.

Reference List

Abad, V., & Williams, K. (2007). Early intervention music therapy: Reporting on a 3-year project to address needs with at-risk families. *Music Therapy Perspectives, 25,* 52–58.

Abromeit, D. H. (2003). The Newborn Individualized Developmental Care and Assessment Program (NIDCAP) as a model for clinical music therapy interventions with premature infants. *Music Therapy Perspectives, 21,* 60–68.

Ahn, S., & Ashida, S. (2012). Music Therapy for Dementia. *Maturitas, 71*(1), 6–7.

Aigen, K. (2005). *Music-centered Music Therapy.* Gilsum, NH: Barcelona Publishers.

Aigen, K. (2014). *The Study of Music Therapy: Current Issues and Concepts.* New York: Routledge Publishers.

Altenmüller, E., Marco, J., Munte, T. F., & Schneider, S. (2009). Neural reorganization underlies improvement in stroke-induced motor dysfunction by music-supported therapy. *Annals of the New York Academy of Sciences, 1169,* 395–405.

Altenmüller, E. O. (2003). How Many Music Centres Are in the Brain? In I. Peretz & R. Zatorre (Eds.), *The Cognitive Neuroscience of Music.* Oxford: Oxford University Press.

Altenmüller, E. O. (2004). Music in Your Head. *Scientific American Mind, 14*(2), 24–31.

Alvesson, M., & Sköldberg, K. (2008). *Reflexive Methodology: New Vistas for Qualitative Research.* London: Sage Publishers.

Ansdell, G. (1991). Mapping the Territory. *British Journal of Music Therapy, 5*(2), 18–27.

Ansdell, G. (1995). *Music for Life.* London: Jessica Kingsley Publishers.

Ansdell, G. (1996). 'Talking about Music Therapy: a dilemma and a qualitative experiment'. *British Journal of Music Therapy, 10*(1), 4–15.

Ansdell, G. (2002). Community Music Therapy & the Winds of Change. *Voices: A World Forum for Music Therapy.* Retrieved from http://www.voices.no/mainissues/Voices2(2)ansdell.html

Ansdell, G. (2005a). Being Who You Aren't; Doing What You Can't: Community Music Therapy & the Paradoxes of Performance. *Voices: A World Forum for Music Therapy.* Retrieved from http://www.voices.no/mainissues/mi40005000192.html

Ansdell, G. (2005b). Community Music Therapy: A Plea for 'Fuzzy Recognition' Instead of Final Definition. [Contribution to moderated discussions]. *Voices: A World Forum for Music Therapy.* Retrieved from http://voices.no/discussions/discm4_07.html

Ansdell, G. (2006). Evidence & Effectiveness in Music Therapy: What's Appropriate? Why can't it be simple? (Five Complexities). A response to Tia DeNora's 'Evidence and Effectiveness in Music Therapy: Problems, Power, Possibilities, and Performances in Health Contexts'. *British Journal of Music Therapy, 20*(2), 96–99.

Ansdell, G. (2014a). *How Music Helps in Music Therapy and Everyday Life.* Farnham, UK: Ashgate Publishers.

Ansdell, G. (2014b). Revisiting 'CoMT and the Winds of Change' (2002): An Original Article and a Retrospective Evaluation'. *International Journal of Community Music, 7*(1), 11–45.

Ansdell, G., & DeNora, T. (2012). Musical Flourishing: Community Music Therapy, Controversy, and the Cultivation of Wellbeing. In R. MacDonald, G. Kreutz, & L. Mitchell (Eds.), *Music, Health and Wellbeing* (pp. 97–112). Oxford: Oxford University Press.

Ansdell, G., & DeNora, T. (2016). *Musical Pathways in Recovery: Community Music Therapy and Mental Wellbeing.* Farnham: Ashgate Publishers.

Ansdell, G., & Meehan, J. (2010). "Some Light at the End of the Tunnel": Exploring Users' Evidence for the Effectiveness of Music Therapy in Adult Mental Health Settings. *Music and Medicine, 2*(1), 29–40.

Atkinson, J. (2002). *Survey of Community Music in the UK.* [Unpublished report for the Speedwell Trust].

Azoulay, R. (2009). 'A Music Psychotherapy Approach for the Treatment of Adults with Pulmonary Disease. In *Music, the breath and health: Advances in integrative music therapy.* R. Azoulay and J. Loewy, (Eds); pp. 151-168; New York, NY, US: Satchnote Press.

Baker, F., Wigram, T., & Gold, C. (2005). The Effects of a Song-singing Programme on the Affective Speaking Intonation of People with Traumatic Brain Injury. *Brain Injury, 19*(7), 519–528.

Baker, F. A. (2013). Front and Center Stage: Participants Performing Songs Created During Music Therapy. *The Arts in Psychotherapy, 40,* 20–28.

Baines, S. (2000/2003). A Consumer-Directed and Partnered Community Mental Health Music Therapy Program: Program Development and Evaluation. *Canadian Journal of Music Therapy, 7* (1), 51-70.

Baines, S., & Danko, G. (2010). Community Mental Health Music Therapy: A Consumer-Initated Songbased Paradigm. *Canadian Journal of Music Therapy, 16* (1), 148-191.

Ballard, C., Brown, R., Fossey, J., Douglas, S., Bradley, P., Hancock, J., James, I., Juszczak, E., Bentham, P., Burns, A., Lindesay, J., Jacoby, R., O'Brien, J., Bullock, R., Johnson, T., Holmes, C., and Howard, R. (2009). Brief Psychosocial Therapy for the Treatment of Agitation in Alzheimer's Disease (The CALM-AD Trial). *American Journal of Geriatric Psychiatry, 17* (9), 726-73.

Baker, F., Dingle, G., and Gleadhill, L. (2012). 'Must be the ganja': Using rap music in music therapy for substance use disorders. Therapeutic uses of rap and hip-hop. In S. Hadley and G. Yancy (Eds.); pp. 321-336; New York, NY, US: Routledge/Taylor & Francis.

Barrington, A. (2005). *Music Therapy: A Study in Professionalisation.* (Unpublished doctoral dissertation). University of Durham, UK.

Barrington, A. (2008). Challenging the Profession. *British Journal of Music Therapy, 22*(2), 65–72.

Baxter, H. T., Berghofer, J. A., MacEwan, L., Nelson, J., Peters, K., & Roberts, P. (2007). *The Individualized Music Therapy Assessment Profile.* London: Jessica Kingsley Publishers.

Beard, R. (2012). Art Therapies and Dementia Care: A Systematic Review. *Dementia, 11*(5), 633–656.

Belgrave, M. (2011). The Effect of a Music Therapy Intergenerational Program on Children and Older Adult's Intergenerational Interactions, Cross-age Attitudes, and Older Adults' Psychosocial Well- being. *Journal of Music Therapy, 48*(4), 486-508.

Boso, M., Emanuele, E., Minazzi, V., Abbamonte, M., & Politi, P. (2007). Effect of Long-Term Interactive Music Therapy on Behavior Profile and Musical Skills in Young Adults with Severe Autism. *The Journal of Alternative and Complementary Medicine, 13*(7), 709–712.

Botello, K., & Krout, R. (2008). Music Therapy Assessment of Automatic Thoughts: Developing a Cognitive Behavioral Application of Improvisation to Assess Couple Communication. *Music Therapy Perspectives, 26*(1), 51–55.

Brandalise, A. (2015). Music Therapy and Theatre: A Community Music Therapy Socio-Cultural Proposal for the Inclusion of Persons

With Autism Spectrum Disorders. *Voices: A World Forum For Music Therapy, 15*(1). doi:10.15845/voices.v1i1.733

Brandes, V., Terris, D. D., Fischer, C., Loerbroks, A., Jarczok, M. N., Ottowitz, G., Titscher, G., Fischer, J. E., & Thayer, J. F.(2010). Receptive Music Therapy for the Treatment of Depression: A Controlled Clinical Trial of Efficacy. *Psychotherapy and Psychosomatics, 79,* 321–322.

Brown, S., Götell, E., & Ekmann, S. (2001a). Singing as a Therapeutic Intervention in Dementia Care. *Western Journal of Nursing Research, 24*(2), 195–216.

Brown, S., Götell, E., & Ekmann, S. (2001b). 'Music-therapeutic caregiving': the necessity of active music-making in clinical care. *The Arts in Psychotherapy, 28,* 125–135.

Brown, S., Götell, E., & Ekman, S. (2001c). Singing as a therapeutic intervention in dementia care. *Journal of Dementia Care, 9*(4), 33–37.

Bruscia, K. (1987). *Improvisational Models of Music Therapy*. Springfield, IL: Charles C. Thomas Publisher.

Bruscia, K. (1998). *Defining Music Therapy* (2nd ed.). Gilsum, NH: Barcelona Publishers.

Care Quality Commission. (2015). *Annual Report*. London: Care Quality Commission.

Carpente, J. (2013). *The Individual Music-Centered Assessment Profile for Neurodevelopmental Disorders (IMCAP-ND): A Clinical Manual*. New York: Regina Publishers.

Carr, C., d'Ardenne, P., Sloboda, A., Scott, C., Wang, D., & Priebe, S. (2012). Group Music Therapy for Patients with Persistent Post-traumatic Stress Disorder: An Exploratory Randomized Controlled Trial with Mixed Methods Evaluation. *Psychology and Psychotherapy: Theory, Research and Practice, 85*(2), 179–202.

Cassidy, J. W. (2009). The Effect of Decibel Level of Music Stimuli and Gender on Head Circumference and Physiological Responses of Premature Infants in the NICU. *Journal of Music Therapy, 46*(3), 180–190.

Ceccato, E., Vigato, G., Bonetto, C., Bevilacqua, A., Pizziolo, P., Crociani, S., Zanfretta, E., Pollini, L., Caneva, P.A., Baldin, L., Frongillo, C., Signorini, A., Demoro, S., and Barchi, E. (2012). STAM Protocol in Dementia: A Multicenter, Single-blind, Randomized, and Controlled Trial. *American Journal of Alzheimers Disease and Other Dementias,* 27 (5), 301-310.

Chaffin, R., & Imreh, G. (2001). A Comparison of Practice and Self-report as Sources of Information About the Goals of Expert Practice. *Psychology of Music, 29,* 36–69.

Chan, M.F., Chan, E.A., Mok, E., and Kwan, Tse, F.Y. (2009). Effect of music on depression levels and physiological responses in community-based older adults. *International Journal of Mental Health Nursing,* 18 (4), 285-294.

Chlan, L., & Heiderscheit, A. (2009). A Tool for Music Preference Assessment in Critically Ill Patients Receiving Mechanical Ventilatory Support. *Music Therapy Perspectives, 27*(1), 42–47.

Choi, A. N., Lee, M. S., Cheong, K. J., & Lee, J. S. (2009). Effects of Group Music Intervention on Behavioral and Psychological Symptoms in Patients with Dementia: A Pilot-Controlled Trial. *International Journal of Neuroscience, 119*(4), 471–481.

Choi, A. N., Lee, M. S., & Lim, H. J. (2008). Effects of group music intervention on depression, anxiety, and relationships in psychiatric patients: a pilot study. *Journal of Alternative and Complementary Medicine, 14*(5), 567–570.

Cilliers, P. (1998). *Complexity and Postmodernism: Understanding Complex Systems.* London: Routledge Publishers.

Clair, A. A., Mathews, R., & Kosloski, K. (2005). Assessment of Active Music Participation as an Indication of Subsequent Music-making Engagement for Persons with Midstage Dementia. *American Journal of Alzheimer's Disease and Other Dementias, 20*(1), 37–40.

Cohen-Mansfield, J., Thein, K., Dakheel-Ali, M., and Marx, M. (2010). The Underlying Meaning of Stimuli: Impact on Engagement of Persons with Dementia. *Psychiatry Research, 177*(1-2), 216-222.

Colebrook, C. (2008). *Gilles Deleuze.* London: Routledge Publishers.

Concise Oxford English Dictionary. (1999). Oxford: Oxford University Press.

Cooke, M. L., Moyle, W., Shum, D. H., Harrison, S. D., & Murfield, J. E. (2010). A randomized controlled trial exploring the effect of music on agitated behaviours and anxiety in older people with dementia. *Aging and Mental Health, 14*(8), 905–916.

Cross, I. (2001a). Review of The Origins of Music. *Trends in Neurosciences, 24*(3), 190.

Cross, I. (2001b). Music, mind and evolution. *Psychology of Music* *29*(1), 95–102.

Curtis, S. (2000). Singing Subversion, Singing Soul: Women's Voices in Feminist Music Therapy. *Dissertation Abstracts International, 60*(12–A), 4240.

Curtis, S. (2011). Music Therapy and the Symphony: A University-Community Collaborative Project in Palliative Care. *Music and Medicine, 3*(1), 20–26.

Curtis, S. (2012). Music Therapy & Social Justice: A Personal Journey. *Arts & Psychotherapy, 39*(3), 209–213.

Curtis, S. (2015). Profile of Community Music Therapists in North America: A Survey. *Voices: A World Forum for Music Therapy, 15*(1). doi:10.15845/voices.v1i1.811

Curtis, S., & Sigmon Mercado, C. (2004). Community Music Therapy for Citizens with Developmental Disabilities. *Voices: A World Forum for Music Therapy.* Retrieved from http://voices.no/mainissues/mi40004000162.html

Curtis, S., & Vaillancourt, G. (2012). The Children's Right to Music Project. *Voices: A World Forum for Music Therapy.* Retrieved from http://dx.doi.org/10.15845/voices.v12i3.676

Dalton, T. A., & Krout, R. E. (2005). Development of the Grief Process Scale Through Music Therapy Songwriting with Bereaved Adolescents. *The Arts in Psychotherapy, 32,* 131–143.

Darnley-Smith, R. (2013). What is the Music of Music Therapy? An Enquiry into the Aesthetics of Clinical Improvisation. (Unpublished Doctoral dissertation). Durham University, Durham, UK.

Daveson, B. (2010). An Audit About Music Therapy Assessments and Recommendations for Adult Patients Suspected to be in a Low Awareness State. *Journal of Music Therapy, 47*(4), 408-422.

Davies, A., & Sloboda, A. (2009). Turbulence at the Boundary. In H. Odell-Miller and E. Richards (Eds.), *Supervision of Music Therapy.* London: Routledge Publishers.

Daykin, N., Attwood, M., & Willis, J. (2013). Supporting arts and health evaluation: Report of a UK knowledge transfer partnership. *Journal of Applied Arts and Health, 4*(2), 179–190.

Daykin, N., Byrne, E., Soteriou, T., & O'Connor, S. (2010). Arts and mental health: Enhancing mental healthcare environments. *World Health Design, 3*(2), 62–68.

Daykin, N., De Viggiani, N., Pilkington, P., & Moriarty, Y. (2012). Music-making for health, well-being and behaviour change in youth justice settings: A systematic review. *Health Promotion International, 28*(2), 197–210.

Daykin, N., Moriarty, Y., De Viggiani, N., & Pilkington, P. (2011). Evidence review: Music-making with young offenders and young people at risk of offending. *Project Report.* London: Youth Music.

Deleuze, G., & Guattari, F. (1984/2004). *Anti-Oedipus: Capitalism and Schizophrenia.* Minneapolis, MN: University of Minnesota Press.

Deleuze, G., & Guattari, F. (1986). *A Thousand Plateaus: Capitalism and Schizophrenia.* Minneapolis, MN: University of Minnesota Press.

Dennis, P., & Rickson, D. (2014). The Leader of the Band: A Case Story of CoMT on a Hospital Ward for People Who Have Dementia. *Voices: A World Forum for Music Therapy, 14*(1). Retrieved from https://voices.no/index.php/voices/article/view/728/633

DeNora, T. (2000). *Music in Everyday Life.* Cambridge: Cambridge University Press.

DeNora, T. (2003). *After Adorno: Rethinking Music Sociology* Cambridge: Cambridge University Press.

Dickerson, G. (1982). The Community and Music Therapy as a Mental Health Service. Music Therapy—A Service to the Community. Papers read at the one-day conference in Oxford. London: BSMT.

Dureau, S. J. (2005). The Effect of Gender on One-Day-Old Infants Behaviour and Heart Rate Responses to Music Decibel Level. *Journal of Music Therapy, 42*(3), 168–184.

Edwards, J. (2002). 'Music Therapy by any other name would smell as sweet' or 'Community Music Therapy' means 'Culturally Sensitive Music Therapy' in our language'. *Voices: A World Forum for Music Therapy.* Retrieved from http://www.voices.no/discussions/discm8_03.html

Edwards, J. (Ed.). (2011). *Music Therapy and Parent-Infant Bonding.* Oxford: Oxford University Press.

Eyre, L. (2008). Medical Music Therapy and Kidney Disease: The Development of a Clinical Method for Persons Receiving Haemodialysis. *Canadian Journal of Music Therapy, 14*(1), 55-87.

Facet. (2013). In *Oxford English Dictionary.* Retrieved May 13, 2015, from http://www.oed.com/view/Entry/67435?rskey=GSNnuX&result=2#eid

Fischer-Terworth, C., & Probst, P. (2011). Evaluation of a TEACCH- and Music Therapy–based Psychological Intervention in Mild to Moderate Dementia: A Controlled Trial. *The Journal of Gerontopsychology and Geriatric Psychiatry, 24*(2), 93–101.

Fouché, S., & Torrance, K. (2005). Lose Yourself in the Music, the Moment, Yo! Music Therapy with an Adolescent Group Involved in Gangsterism. *Voices: A World Forum for Music Therapy, 5*(3). Retrieved from https://voices.no/index.php/voices/article/view/232

Gardstrom, S., Carlini, M, Josefczyk, J., and Love, A. (2013). Women with addictions: Music therapy clinical postures and interventions. *Music Therapy Perspectives, 31*(2), pp. 95-104.

Garland, K., Beer, E., Eppingstall, B., & O'Connor, D. W. (2007). A comparison of two treatments of agitated behavior in nursing home residents with dementia: simulated family presence and preferred music. *Am. J. Geriatr. Psychiatry, 15*(6), 514–521.

Gerdner, L. (2000). Effects of Individualized versus Classical "relaxation" Music on the Frequency of Agitation in Elderly Persons with Alzheimer's Disease and Related Disorders. *International Psychogeriatrics, 12* (1), 49-65.

Gilbertson, S. (2008). The Silent Epidemic of Road Traffic Injury: What Can Music Therapists do About it? *Voices: A World Forum for Music Therapy, 8*(1). Retrieved from http://voices.no/index.php/ voices/article/view/448/366

Gilroy, A., & Lee, C. (1995). *Art and Music: Therapy and Research.* London: Routledge Publishers.

Gold, C., Voracek, M., & Wigram, T. (2004). Effects of Music Therapy for Children and Adolescents with Psychopathology: A Meta-analysis. *Journal of Child Psychology and Psychiatry, 45*(6), 1054–1063.

Goodchild, P. (1996). *Deleuze and Guattari: An Introduction to the Politics of Desire.* London: Sage Publishers.

Gooding, L.F. (2011). The Effect of a Music Therapy Social Skills Training Program on Improving Social Competence in Children and Adolescents with Social Skills Deficits. *Journal of Music Therapy,* 48 (4): 440-462. doi: 10.1093/jmt/48.4.440

Gooding, L.F., & Gregory, D. (2011). Descriptive Analysis of YouTube Music Therapy Videos. *Journal of Music Therapy, 48*(3), 357–369.

Götell, E., Brown, S., & Ekman, S-L. (2000). Caregiver-assisted music events in psychogeriatric care. *Journal of Psychiatric and Mental Health Nursing, 7,* 119–125.

Götell, E., Brown, S., & Ekman, S-L. (2002). Caregiver Singing and Background Music in Dementia Care. *Western Journal of Nursing Research, 24*(2), 195–216.

Götell, E., Brown, S., & Ekman, S-L. (2003). Influence of caregiver singing and background music on posture, movement and sensory awareness in dementia care. *International Psychogeriatrics, 15*(4), 411–430.

Götell, E., Brown, S., & Ekman, S-L. (2009). The influence of caregiver singing and background music on vocally expressed emotions and moods in dementia care: A qualitative analysis. *International Journal of Nursing Studies, 46,* 422–430.

Griggs-Drane, E. (2009). The use of musical wind instruments with patients who have pulmonary diseases: Clinical recommendations for music therapists. In *Music, the Breath and Health: Advances in integrative music therapy.* R. Azoulay, and J. Loewy, (Eds.); pp. 103-115; New York, NY, US: Satchnote Press.

Grocke, D., Bloch, S., & Castle, D. (2008). Is There a Role for Music Therapy in the Care of the Severely Mentally Ill? *Australasian Psychiatry, 16*(6), 442–445.

Guétin, S., Portet, F., Picot, M. C., Pommi, C., Messaoudi, M., Djabelkir, L., Olsen, A. L., Cano, M. M., Lecourt, E., & Touchon, J. (2009). Effect of music therapy on anxiety and depression in patients with Alzheimer's-type dementia: randomised, controlled study. *Dementia and Geriatric Cognitive Disorders, 28*(1), 36–46.

Hammar, M. L., Emami, A., Engström, G., & Götell, E. (2011a). Finding the key to communion. Caregivers' experience of music therapeutic caregiving in dementia care. A qualitative analysis. *Dementia, 10*(1), 98–111.

Hammar, M. L., Emami, A., Engström, G., &d Götell, E. (2011b). Reactions of Persons with dementia to caregivers singing in morning care situations. *The Open Nursing Journal* (open access). Published Nov. 23, 2010.

Hammar, M. L., Emami, A., Engström, G., & Götell, E. (2011c). Communicating through caregiver singing during morning care situations. *Scandinavian Journal of Caring Sciences, 25*(1), 160–168.

Hammar, M. L., Götell, E., Emami, A., & Engström, G. (2011). The impact of caregivers' singing on expression of emotion and resistance during morning care situations in persons with dementia. *Journal of Clinical Nursing, 20*(7–8), 969–978.

Hanser, S., and Mandel, S. (2014). Harmony of the heart: Music therapy. Investigations of music therapy in cardiac rehabilitation. *Musik-, Tanz- und Kunsttherapie*, 25(1), pp. 3-8.

Harris, P., and Caporella, C.A. (2014). An intergenerational choir formed to lessen Alzheimer's disease stigma in college students and decrease the social isolation of people with Alzheimer's disease and their family members: A pilot study. *American Journal of Alzheimer's Disease and Other Dementias*, 29 (3), pp. 270-281.

Hilliard, R. E. (2001). The Effects of Music Therapy-based Bereavement Groups on Mood and Behaviour of Grieving Children: A Pilot Study. *Journal of Music Therapy, 38*(4), 291–306.

Hillier, A., Greher, G., Poto, N., & Dougherty, M. (2012). Postive Outcomes Following Participation in a Music Intervention for Adolescents and Young Adults on the Autism Spectrum. *Psychology of Music, 40*(2), 201–215.

Hintz, M. (2000). Geriatric Music Therapy Clinical Assessment: Assessment of Music Skills and Related Behaviors. *Music Therapy Perspectives, 18*(1), 31–40.

Ho, S.Y., Lai, H.L., Jeng, S.Y., Tang, C.W., Sung, H.C., and Chen, P.W. (2011). The Effects of Researcher-Composed Music at Mealtime on Agitation in Nursing Home Residents with Dementia. *Archives of Psychiatric Nursing, 25*(6), 49-55.

Holmes, C., Knights, A., Dean C., Hodkinson, S., & Hopkins, V. (2006). Keep music live: music and the alleviation of apathy in dementia subjects. *International Psychogeriatrics, 18*(4), 623–630.

Hussey, D., Reed, A., Layman, D., and Pasiali, V. (2006). Music therapy and complex trauma: A protocol for developing social reciprocity. *Residential Treatment for Children & Youth*, 24(1-2), pp. 111-129.

Huang, S. T., Good, M., & Zauszniewski, J. A. (2010). The effectiveness of music in relieving pain in cancer patients: a randomized controlled trial. *International Journal of Nursing Studies, 47*(11), 1354–1362.

Hulme, C., Wright, J., Crocker, T., Oluboyede, Y., & House, A. (2010). Non-pharmocological Approaches for Dementia that Informal

Carers Might Try or Access: A Systematic Review. *International Journal of Geriatric Psychiatry, 25*(7), 756–763.

Iliya, Y. (2011). Singing for healing and hope: Music therapy methods that use the voice with individuals who are homeless and mentally ill. *Music Therapy Perspectives, 29*(1), pp. 14-22.

Jacobsen, S. (2009). Music Therapy Assessment as Evaluation and Validation: Commentary on Lagan's Article, 2009. *Australian Journal of Music Therapy, 20.*

Jacobsen, S., & Wigram, T. (2007). Music Therapy for the Assessment of Parental Competencies for Children in Need of Care. *Nordic Journal of Music Therapy, 16*(2).

Jampel, P. (2006). Performance in Music Therapy with Mentally Ill Adults. (Unpublished doctoral dissertation). New York University, New York.

Jampel, P. (2011). Performance in Music Therapy: Experiences in Five Dimensions. *Voices: A World Forum for Music Therapy, 11*(1). Retrieved from https://normt.uib.no/index.php/voices/article/view/275/440

Johnson, S. (2001). *Emergence.* London: Penguin Publishers.

Jones, J. (2014). Health Musicking in Skiffle Steel Orchestra: Thoughts on Collaboration between Community Music Therapy and Medical Ethnomusicology. *International Journal of Community Music, 7*(1), 129–144.

Karagozoglu, S., Tekyasar, F., & Yilmaz, F. A. (2013). Effects of Music Therapy and Guided Visual Imagery on Chemotherapy-induced Anxiety and Nausea-vomiting. *Journal of Clinical Nursing, 22*(1–2), 39–50.

Kenny, C. (1982). *The Mythic Artery: The Magic of Music Therapy.* Atascadero, CA: Ridgeview Publishing Company.

Kenny, C. (1985). Music: A Whole Systems Approach. *Music Therapy, 5*(1), 3–11.

Kenny, C. (1989). *The Field of Play: A Guide for the Theory and Practice of Music Therapy.* Atascadero, CA: Ridgeview Publishing Company.

Kenny, C. (1996). The Story of the Field of Play. In J. Langenberg, K. Aigen, & J. Frommer (Eds.), *Qualitative Music Therapy Research: Beginning Dialogues.* Gilsum, NH: Barcelona Publishers.

Kenny, C. (1999). Beyond This Point There Be Dragons: Developing General Theory in Music Therapy. *Nordic Journal of Music Therapy, 5*(1), 31–32.

Kenny, C., & Stige, B. (2002). *Contemporary Voices in Music Therapy, Communication, Culture and Community*. Oslo: Unipub Forlag.

Kenny, C. (2006). *Music and Life in the Field of Play*. Gilsum, NH: Barcelona Publishers.

Kern, P., Wakeford, L., & Aldridge, D. (2007). Improving the Performance of a Young Child with Autism During Self-Care Tasks Using Embedded Song Interventions: A Case Study. *Music Therapy Perspectives, 25*(1), 43–51.

Khan, F., & Curtice, M. (2011). Non-pharmacological Management of Behavioural Symptoms of Dementia. *British Journal of Community Nursing, 16*(9), 441–449.

Kim, S. J. (2010). Music Therapy Protocol Development to Enhance Swallowing Training for Stroke Patients with Dysphagia. *Journal of Music Therapy, 47*(2), 102–119.

Kim, M., & Tomaino, C. M. (2008). Protocol Evaluation for Effective Music Therapy for Persons with Non-fluent Aphasia. *Topics in Stroke Rehabilitation, 15*(6), 555–569.

Kittay, J. (2008). The Sound Surround. *Nordic Journal of Music Therapy, 17*(1), 41–54.

Kristjánsdóttir, Ó., & Kristjánsdóttir, G. (2011). Randomized Clinical Trial of Musical Distraction With and Without Headphones for Adolescents' Immunization Pain. *Scandinavian Journal of Caring Sciences, 25*(1), 19–26.

Krüger, V. and Stige, B. (2015). Between rights and realities—Music as a structuring resource in child welfare everyday life: A qualitative study. *Nordic Journal of Music Therapy*, *24*(2), 99-122.

Lane-Brown, A. T., & Tate, R. L. (2009). Apathy After Acquired Brain Impairment: A Systematic Review of Non-Pharmacological Interventions. *Neuropsychological Rehabilitation, 19*(4), 481–516.

Langhan, D. (2009). A Music Therapy Assessment Tool for Special Education: Incorporating Education Outcomes. *Australian Journal of Music Therapy, 20*, 78–98.

Latour, B. (1993). *We Have Never Been Modern*. Cambridge, MA: MIT Press.

Latour, B. (2005). *Reassembling the Social*. Oxford: Oxford University Press.

Latour, B. (2010). *The Making of Law: An Ethnography of the Conseil D'État.* Cambridge, UK: Polity Press.

Latour, B., & Woolgar, S. (1979). *Laboratory Life: The Construction of Scientific Facts.* Princeton, NJ: Princeton University Press.

Law, J. (2004). *After Method: Mess in Social Science Research.* Oxford: Routledge Publishers.

Law, J. (2008). On Sociology and STS. Available at http://www.heterogeneities.net/publications/Law2008OnSociolog yAndSTS.pdf

Law, J., & Mol, A. (2002). *Complexities.* Durham, NC: Duke University Press.

Ledger, A., & Baker, F. (2007). An investigation of long-term effects of group music therapy on agitation levels of people with Alzheimer's Disease. *Ageing & Mental Health, 11*(3), 330–338.

Leist, C. (2011). 'A Music Therapy Support Group to Ameliorate Psychological Distress in Adults with Coronary Heart Disease in a Rural Community. Dissertation Abstracts International Section A: Humanities and Social Sciences, *72*(6-A), 1828.

Lim, H. A. (2010). Effect of "Developmental Speech and Language Training Through Music" on Speech Production in Children with Autism Spectrum Disorders. *Journal of Music Therapy, 47*(1), 2–26.

Lin, Y., Chu, H., Yang, C. Y., Chen, C. H., Chen, S. G., Chang, H. J., Hsieh, C. J., & Chou, K. R. (2011a). Effectiveness of group music intervention against agitated behavior in elderly persons with dementia. *International Journal of Geriatric Psychiatry, 26*(7), 670–678.

Locke, J. M., & Mudford, O. C. (2010). Using Music to Decrease Disruptive Vocalizations in a Man with Dementia. *Behavioral Interventions, 25(3),* 253–260.

Loewy, J. V. (1995). The Musical Stages of Speech: A Developmental Model of Pre-Verbal Sound Making. *Music Therapy, 13*(1), 47–73.

MacDonald, R., Kreutz, G., & Mitchell, L. (Eds.). (2012). *Music, Health & Wellbeing.* Oxford: Oxford University Press.

Magee, W. (2007a). Music as a Diagnostic Tool in Low Awareness States: Considering Limbic Responses. *Brain Injury, 21*(6), 593–599.

Magee, W. (2007b). Development of a Music Therapy Assessment Tool for Patients in Low Awareness States. *Neurorehabilitation, 22*(4), 319–324.

Magee, W., Brumfitt, S. M., Freeman, M., & Davidson, J. (2006). The Role of Music Therapy in an Interdisciplinary Approach to Address Functional Communication in Complex Neuro-Communication Disorders: A Case Report. *Disability and Rehabilitation, 28*(19), 1221–1229.

Magill, L. (2009). The Meaning of the Music: The Role of Music in Palliative Care Music Therapy as Perceived by Bereaved Caregivers of Advanced Cancer Patients. *American Journal of Hospice & Palliative Care, 26*(1), 33–39.

Mahoney, J. (2010). Inter-rater Agreement on the Nordoff-Robbins Evaluation Scale I: Client-Therapist Relationship in Musical Activity. *Music and Medicine, 2*(1), 23–28.

Malloch, S., & Trevarthen, C. (2009). *Communicative Musicality.* Oxford: Oxford University Press.

Mandel, S., Hanser, S., Secic, M., and Davis, B.(2007). Effects of music therapy on health-related outcomes in cardiac rehabilitation: A randomized controlled trial. *Journal of Music Therapy, 44*(3), 176-197.

Maratos, A. (2004). Whatever Next? Community Music Therapy for the Institution! In M. Pavlicevic & G. Ansdell (Eds.), *CoMT*. London: Jessica Kingsley Publishers.

Maue-Johnson, E., & Tanguay, C. (2006). Assessing the Unique Needs of Hospice Patients: A Tool for Music Therapists. *Music Therapy Perspectives, 24*(1), 13–20.

Mays, K., Clark, D., and Gordon, A. (2008). Treating addiction with tunes: A systematic review of music therapy for the treatment of patients with addictions. *Substance Abuse, 29*(4), 51-59.

Mercado, C., & Mercado, E. (2006). A Program Using Environmental Manipulation, Music Therapy Activities, and the Somatron Vibroacoustic Chair to Reduce Agitation Behaviours of Nursing Home Residents with Psychiatric Disorders. *Music Therapy Perspectives, 24*(1), 30–38.

Mitchell, L., & MacDonald, R. (2006). An Experimental Investigation of the Effects of Preferred and Relaxing Music on Pain Perception. *Journal of Music Therapy, 43*(4), 295–316.

Mohammadi, A. Z., Shahabi, T., & Panah, F. M. (2011). An Evaluation of the Effect of Group Music Therapy on Stress, Anxiety, and Depression Levels in Nursing Home Residents. *Canadian Journal of Music Therapy, 17*(1), 55-68.

Mol, A. (2002). *The Body Multiple: Ontology in Medical Practice.* Durham, NC: Duke University Press.

Mongrain, M., & Trambakoulos, J. (2007). A Musical Mood Induction Alleviates Dysfunctional Attitudes in Needy and Self-Critical Individuals. *Journal of Cognitive Psychotherapy, 21*(4), 295–309.

Morgan, K., Bartrop, R., Telfer, J., & Tennant, C. (2011). A Controlled Trial Investigating the Effect of Music Therapy During an Acute Psychiatric Episode. *Acta Psychiatr. Scand., 124*, 363–371.

Mrázová, M., & Celec, P. (2010). A systematic review of randomized controlled trials using music therapy for children. *Journal of Alternative and Complementary Medicine, 16*(10), 1089–1095.

Munk-Madsen, N. M. (2001). Assessment in Music Therapy with Clients Suffering from Dementia. *Nordic Journal of Music Therapy, 10*(2), 205–208.

Munte T. F., Altenmüller, E., & Jancke, L. (2002). The Musician's Brain as a Model of Neuroplasticity. *Nat. Rev. Neurosci., 3*, 473–478.

Myskja, A. (2005). Therapeutic Use of Music in Nursing Homes. *Tidsskrift for den Norske Laegeforening: Tidsskrift for Praktisk Medecin, 125*(11), 1497–1499.

Naess, T., & Ruud, E. (2007). Audible Gestures: From Clinical Improvisation to Community Music Therapy. *Nordic Journal of Music Therapy, 16*(2), 160–171.

Nair, B.K., Heim, C., Krishnan, C., D'Este, C., Marley, J., and Attia, J. (2011). The Effect of Baroque Music on Behavioural Disturbances in Patients with Dementia, *Australasian Journal of Ageing, 30* (1), 11-15.

Nancy, J. L. (2005). *The Ground of the Image.* New York: Fordham University Press.

Nancy, J. L. (2007). *Listening.* New York: Fordham University Press.

Nayak, S., Shiflett, S., Eshun, S., & Levine, F. (2000). Culture and Gender Effects in Pain Beliefs and the Prediction of Pain Tolerance. *Cross Cultural Research, 34*(2), 135–151.

Ng, W. F. (2011). Can Music Therapy be an Answer to the Terrorist Question? A Singaporean Music Therapist's Perspective. *Voices:*

A World Forum for Music Therapy, 11(1). Retrieved from https://voices.no/index.php/voices/article/view/564/444

NICE-SCIE (2006). *Dementia: Supporting People with Dementia and their Carers in Health and Social Care.* London: National Institute for Health and Care Excellence.

Nordoff, P., & Robbins, C. (1971). *Therapy in Music for Handicapped Children.* London: Victor Gollancz Publishers.

Nordoff, P., & Robbins, C. (1977). *Creative Music Therapy: Individualized treatment for the handicapped child.* New York: John Day Publishers.

Nordoff, P., & Robbins, C. (2007). *Creative Music Therapy: A Guide to fostering clinical musicianship* (2nd ed., revised and expanded). Gilsum, NH: Barcelona Publishers.

Norman, R. (2012). Music Therapy Assessment of Older Adults in Nursing Homes. *Music Therapy Perspectives, 30*(1), 8–16.

O'Callaghan, C. (2009). Objectivist and Constructivist Music Therapy Research in Oncology and Palliative Care: An Overview and Reflection. *Music and Medicine, 1*(1), 41–60.

O'Callaghan, C., Hudson, P., & Zalcberg, J. (2013). Sound Continuing Bonds with the Deceased: The Relevance of Music, Including Preloss Music Therapy, for Eight Bereaved Caregivers. *Death Studies, 37*(2), 101–125.

O'Grady, L., & McFerran, K. (2007). CoMT and Its Relationship to Community Music: Where Does It End? *Nordic Journal of Music Therapy, 16*(1), 14–26.

O'Kelly, J., & Koffman, J. (2007). Mulitdisciplinary Perspectives of Music Therapy in Adult Palliative Care. *Palliative Medicine, 21*(3), 235–241.

Oddy, N. (2005). Convergences: Possibilities for Therapeutic Intervention in a Large Scale Community Performance. *Voices: A World Forum for Music Therapy.* Retrieved from http://www.voices.no/mainissues/mi40005000187.html

Odell-Miller, H. (1995). Why provide music therapy in the community for adults with mental health problems? *British Journal of Music Therapy, 9*(1).

Oosthuizen, H., Fouché, S., & Torrance, K. (2007). Collaborative Work: Negotiations between Music Therapists and Community Musicians in the Development of a South African Community Music Therapy Project. *Voices: A World Forum for Music Therapy,*

7(3). Retrieved from http://voices.no/indexphp/voices/article/view/546

Park, J., & Hughes, A. K. (2012). Nonpharmocological Approaches to the Management of Chronic Pain in Community-Dwelling Older Adults: A Review of Empirical Evidence. *Journal of the American Geriatrics Society, 60,* 555–568.

Pasiali, V. (2012). Supporting parent-child interactions: Music therapy as an intervention for promoting mutually responsive orientation. *Journal of Music Therapy, 49,* 303–334.

Pavlicevic, M. (1997). *Music Therapy in Context.* London: Jessica Kingsley Publishers.

Pavlicevic, M., & Ansdell, G. (Eds.). (2004). *Community Music Therapy.* London: Jessica Kingsley Publishers.

Pavlicevic, M., & Ansdell, G. (2009). Between Communicative Musicality and Collaborative Musicing: Perspectives from Community Music Therapy. In S. Malloch & C. Trevarthen (Eds.), *Communicative Musicality* (pp. 357–376). Oxford: Oxford University Press.

Pavlicevic, M., & Fouché, S. (2014). Reflections from the Market Place- Community Music Therapy in Context. *International Journal of Community Music, 7*(1), 57–74.

Peretz, I. & Zatorre, R. (2003). *The Cognitive Neuroscience of Music.* Oxford: Oxford University Press.

Phillips-Salimi, C., Stickler, M., Stegenga, K., Lee, M., & Haase, J. (2011). Principles and Strategies for Monitoring Data Collection Integrity in a Multi-Site Randomized Clinical Trial of a Behavioural Intervention. *Research in Nursing Health, 34*(4), 362–371.

Pickett, M. (1976). Music Therapy from the Psychiatric Hospital to the Community. Music Therapy in the Community. Papers read at the conference held in London, 1976. London: BSMT.

Powell, H. (2006). The Voice of Experience: evaluation of music therapy with older people, including those with dementia, in community locations. *British Journal of Music Therapy, 20*(2), 109–120.

Procter, S. (2002). Empowering and Enabling: Music Therapy in Nonmedical Mental Health Provision. In C. Kenny & B. Stige (Eds.), *Contemporary Voices in Music Therapy.* Oslo: Unipub Forlag.

Procter, S. (2006). Whose Evidence? *British Journal of Music Therapy, 20*(2), 74–75.

Procter, S. (2011). Reparative musicing: Thinking on the usefulness of social capital theory within music therapy. *Nordic Journal of Music Therapy, 20*(3), 242-262.

Raglio, A., Bellelli, G., Traficante, D., Gianotti, M., Ubezio, M., Villani, D., & Trabucchi, M. (2008). Efficacy of Music Therapy in the Treatment of Behavioral and Psychiatric Symptoms of Dementia. *Alzheimer's Disease & Associated Disorders, 22*(2), 158–162.

Raglio, A., Bellelli, G., Mazzola, P., Bellandi, D., Giovagnoli, A., Farina, E., Stramba-Badiale, M., Gentile, S., Gianelli, M., Ubezio, M., Zanetti, O., & Trabucchi, M. (2012). Music, Music Therapy and Dementia: A Review of Literature and the Recommendations of the Italian Psychogeriatric association. *Maturitas, 72*(4), 305–310.

Rancière, J. (2007). *The Future of the Image.* London/New York: Verso Press.

Register, D. M., & Hilliard, R. E. (2008). Using Orff-based Techniques in Children's Bereavement Groups: A Cognitive-Behavioural Music Therapy Approach. *The Arts in Psychotherapy, 35*(2), 162–170.

Ridder, H. (2005). An Overview of Therapeutic Initiatives when Working with persons Suffering from Dementia. In D. Aldridge (Ed.), *Music Therapy and Neurological Rehabilitation: Performing Health* (pp. 63–85). London: Jessica Kingsley Publishers

Robb, S. L., Burns, D. S., & Carpenter, J. (2011). Reporting Guidelines for Music-based Interventions. *Journal of Health Psychology, 16*(2), 342–352.

Rolvsjord, R. (2006). Whose power of music? A discussion on music and power-relations in music therapy. *British Journal of Music Therapy, 20*(1), 5–12.

Rolvsjord, R. (2010). *Resource-oriented Music Therapy in Mental Health Care.* Gilsum, NH: Barcelona Publishers.

Romo, R., & Gifford, L. (2007). A Cost-Benefit Analysis of Music Therapy in a Home Hospice. *Nursing Economics, 25*(6), 353–358.

Ruud, E. (1987/1990). *Music as Communication and Interaction: Theoretical Perspectives on Music Therapy.* Oslo: Solum Press.

Ruud, E. (1998). *Music Therapy: Improvisation, Communication and Culture.* Gilsum, NH: Barcelona Publishers.

Ruud, E. (2004). Defining Community Music Therapy. [Contribution to Moderated Discussions]. *Voices: A World Forum for Music Therapy, Moderated Discussion.* Retrieved from http://voices.no/discussions/discm4_04.html

Ruud, E. (2010). *Music Therapy: A Perspective from the Humanities.* Gilsum, NH: Barcelona Publishers.

Ruud, E. (2012). The New Health Musicians. In R. MacDonald, G. Kreutz, & L. Mitchell (Eds.), *Music, Health and Wellbeing.* Oxford: Oxford University Press.

Scalenghe, R., & Murphy, K. (2000). Music Therapy Assessment in the Managed Care Environment. *Music Therapy Perspectives, 18,* 23–30.

Scheiby, B. (2002). Caring for the Caregivers: Trauma, Improvised Music and Transformation of Terror into Meaning Through CoMT Training. In J. Loewy & A. Frish Hara (Eds.), *Caring for the Caregiver: The Use of Music and Music Therapy in Grief and Trauma.* Silver Spring, MD: AMTA.

Schlaug, G., Marchina, S., & Norton, A. (2008). From Singing to Speaking: Why Singing May Lead to Recovery of Expressive Language Function in Patients with Broca's Aphasia. *Music Perception, 25*(4), 315–323.

Shoemark, H. (2008). Mapping Progress within an Individual Music Therapy Session with Full-Term Hospitalized Infants. *Music Therapy Perspectives, 26*(1), 38–45.

Shoshensky, R. (2011). Everybody is a Star: Recording, Performing, and Community Music Therapy. *Music Therapy Perspectives, 29*(1), 23–30.

Silverman, M. J. (2011a). The effect of songwriting on knowledge of coping skills and working alliance in psychiatric patients: a randomized clinical effectiveness study. *Journal of Music Therapy, 48*(1), 103–122.

Silverman, M.J. (2011b) Effects of music therapy on change and depression on clients in detoxification. *Journal of Addictions Nursing, 22*(4), 185-192.

Silverman, M.J., (2011c). Effects of music therapy on change readiness and craving in patients on a detoxification unit. *Journal of Music Therapy*, *48*(4), 509-531.

Silverman, M.J. (2012). Effects of group songwriting on motivation and readiness for treatment on patients in detoxification: A randomized wait-list effectiveness study. Journal of Music Therapy, *49*(4), 414-429.

Silverman, M.J. (2015). Effects of lyric analysis interventions on treatment motivation in patients on a detoxification unit: A randomized

effectiveness study. *Journal of Music Therapy, 52*(1), 117-
134.

Snow, S., & D'Amico, M. (2008). Interdisciplinary Research Through
Community Music Therapy and Performance Ethnography.
Canadian Journal of Music Therapy, 14, 30–46.

Snow, S., & D'Amico, M. (Eds.). (2009). *Assessment in the Creative Arts
Therapies: Designing and Adapting Assessment Tools for Adults
with Developmental Disabilities.* Springfield, IL: Charles C.
Thomas Publisher.

Solli, H., Rolvsjord, R., and Borg, M. (2013). Toward understanding music
therapy as a recovery-oriented practice within mental health care:
A meta-synthesis of service users' experiences. *Nordic Journal of
Music Therapy, 50*(4), 244-273.

Stern, D. (1985). *The Interpersonal World of the Infant.* New York: Basic
Books.

Stewart, K. (2009). Dimensions of the Voice: The Use of Voice and Breath
with Infants and Caregivers in the NICU. In R. Azoulay & J.
Loewy (Eds.), *Music. The Breath and Health: Advances in
Integrative Music Therapy* (pp. 235–250). New York: Satchnote
Press.

Stige, B. (1993). Ngoma, musirør og anna rør [Ngoma, Music and
Movement]. Unpublished Thesis, Øslandets Musikkonservat-
orium, Section for Music Therapy. Oslo, Norway.

Stige, B. (2001). Beyond Objectivism and Relativism? *Nordic Journal of
Music Therapy, 10*(1), 2.

Stige, B. (2002). *Culture-Centred Music Therapy.* Gilsum, NH: Barcelona
Publishers.

Stige, B. (2003). *Elaborations toward a Notion of Community Music
Therapy.* Oslo: Faculty of Arts, University of Oslo.

Stige, B (2014). Community Music Therapy and the Process of Learning
About and Struggling for Openness. *International Journal of
Community Music, 7*(1), 47–55.

Stige, B., & Aarø, L. E. (2012). *Invitation to Community Music Therapy.*
New York: Routledge Publishers.

Stige, B., Ansdell, G., Elefant, C., & Pavlicevic, M. (2010). *Where Music
Helps, Community Music Therapy in Action and Reflection.* Surrey,
UK: Ashgate Publishers.

Streeter, E. (1999). Finding a balance between Psychological Thinking and Musical Awareness in Music Therapy Theory—a Psychoanalytic Perspective. *British Journal of Music Therapy, 13*(1), 5–20.

Streeter, E. (2006). Response to "Music psychotherapy and CoMT: Questions and considerations." *Voices: A World Forum of Music Therapy.* Retrieved from https://voices.no/index.php/ voices/ article/ view/208/ 152

Sung, H. C., Chang, A. M., & Lee, W. L. (2010). A preferred music listening intervention to reduce anxiety in older adults with dementia in nursing homes. *Journal of Clinical Nursing, 19*(7–8), 1056–1064.

Suzuki, M., Kanamori, M., Watanabe, M., Nagasawa, S., Kojima, E., Ooshiro, H., et al. (2004). Behavioural and Endocrinological Evaluation of Music Therapy for Elderly Patients with Dementia. *Nursing and Health Sciences, 6,* 11–18.

Takahashi, T., & Matsushita, H. (2006). Long-term Effects of Music Therapy on Elderly with Moderate/Severe Dementia. *Journal of Music Therapy, 43*(4), 317–333.

Tamplin, J., Baker, F., Jones, B., Way, A., Lee, S. (2013). 'Stroke a Chord: The Effect of Singing in a Community Choir on Mood and Social Engagement for People Living with Aphasia Following a Stroke. *Neurorehabilitation, 32*(4), 929-941.

Tan, X., Yowler, C.J., Super, D.M., and Fratianne, R.B. (2010). The Efficacy of Music Therapy Protocols for Decreasing Pain, Anxiety, and Muscle Tension Levels During Burn Dressing Changes: A Prospective Randomized Crossover Trial. *Journal of Burn Care Research, 31*(4), 590-597.

Teague, A. K., Hahna, N., & McKinney, S. (2006). Group Music Therapy with Women who have Experienced Intimate Partner Violence. *Music Therapy Perspectives, 24*(2), 80–86.

Travers,C.& Barlett, H. (2011). Silver Memories: Implementation and evaluation of a unique radio program for older people. Aging and Mental Health, *15*(2), 1-9.

Tsiris, G. (2014). CoMT: Controversies, Synergies and Ways Forward. *International Journal of Community Music, 7*(1), 3–9.

Tsiris, G., Pavlicevic, M., & Farrant, C. (2014). *A Guide to Evaluation for Arts Therapists and Art & Health Practitioners.* London: Jessica Kingsley Publishers.

Tuastad, L., and O'Grady, L. (2013). Music therapy inside and outside prison—A freedom practice? *Nordic Journal of Music Therapy, 22*(3), 210-232.

Tuastad, L. and Stige, B. (2015). The revenge of Me and THE BAND'its: A narrative inquiry of identity constructions in a rock band of ex-inmates. *Nordic Journal of Music Therapy, 24*(3), 252-275.

Tuet, R., & Lam, L. (2006). A Preliminary Study of the Effects of Music Therapy on Agitation in Chinese Patients with Dementia. *Hong Kong Journal of Psychiatry, 16*(3), 87–91.

Turner, R., & Ioannides, A. (2009). 'Brain, Music and Musicality: Inferences from neuroimaging'. In S. Malloch and C. Trevarthen (Eds.), *Communicative Musicality*. Oxford University Press: Oxford.

Turry, A. (1999). Performance and Product: Clinical Implications for the Music Therapist. *Music Therapy World.* Retrieved from http://musictherapyworld.net

Turry, A. (2005). Music Psychotherapy and CoMT: Questions and Considerations. *Voices: A World Forum for Music Therapy, 5*(1). Retrieved from http://voices.no/index.php/voices/article/view/208/152

Tyson, F. (1968). The Community Music Therapy Center. In E. Thayer Gaston (Ed.), *Music in Therapy.* New York: Macmillan Publishing.

Tyson, F. (1973). Guidelines Toward the Organization of Clinical Music Therapy Programs in the Community. *Journal of Music Therapy, 10*(3), 113–124.

Ulrich, G., Houtmans, T., & Gold, C. (2007). The additional therapeutic effect of group music therapy for schizophrenic patients: a randomized study. *Acta Psychiatrica Scandinavica, 116*(5), 362–370.

Vaillancourt, G. (2009). Mentoring Apprentice Music Therapists for Peace and Social Justice Through CoMT: An Arts-based Study. (Unpublished doctoral dissertation). Antioch University, NH, USA.

Vaillancourt, G. (2012). Music Therapy: A Community Approach to Social Justice. *Arts in Psychotherapy, 39,* 173–178.

Van de Winckel, A., Feys, H., De Werdt, W., & Dom, R. (2004). 'Cognitive and Behavioural Effects of Music-based Exercises in Patients with Dementia'. *Clinical Rehabilitation, 18,* 253–260.

Van der Greer, E., Vink, A.C., Schols, J.M., & Slaets, J.P. (2009). Music in the Nursing Home: Hitting the Right Note! The Provision of Music to Dementia Patients with Verbal and Vocal Agitation in Dutch Nursing Homes. *International Psychogeriatrics, 21*(1), 86-93.

Wall, M., & Duffy, A. (2010). The Effects of Music Therapy for Older People with Dementia. *British Journal of Nursing, 19*(2), 108-113.

Walworth, D. (2007). The Use of Music Therapy within the SCERTS Model for Children with Autism Spectrum Disorder. *Journal of Music Therapy, 44*(1), 2–22.

Weller, C. M., & Baker, F. A. (2011). The Role of Music Therapy in Physical Rehabilitation: A Systematic Literature Review. *Nordic Journal of Music Therapy, 20*(1), 43–61.

Wheeler, B., Shiflett, S., & Nayak, S. (2003). Effects of Numbers of Sessions and Group or Individual Music Therapy on the Mood and Behaviour of People who have had Strokes or Traumatic Brain Injuries. *Nordic Journal of Music Therapy, 12*(2), 139–151.

Whipple, J., & Lindsay, R. (1999). Music for the Soul: A Music Therapy Program for Battered Women. *Music Therapy Perspectives, 17*(2), 61-68.

Whitehead-Pleaux, A., Baryza, M., & Sheridan, R. (2006). The Effects of Music Therapy on Pediatric Patients' Pain and Anxiety During Donor Site Dressing Change. *Journal of Music Therapy, 43*(2), 136–153.

Wigram, T. (2000). A Method of Music Therapy Assessment for the Diagnosis of Autism and Communication Disorders in Children. *Music Therapy Perspectives, 18*(1), 13–22.

Wilhelm, K. (2004). Music Therapy and Private Practice: Recommendations on Financial Viability and Marketing. *Music Therapy Perspectives, 22*(2), 68–83.

Wilson, S. J., Parsons, K., & Reutens, D. C. (2006). Preserved Singing in Aphasia: A Case Study of the Efficacy of Melodic Intonation Therapy. *Music Perception, 24*(1), 23–35.

Winter, P. (2014). Perspectives on the practice of community music therapy in rural primary schools of Malawi. *Nordic Journal of Music Therapy, 24*(3), 276-287.

Wood, S. (2006). "The Matrix": A Model of Community Music Therapy Processes. *Voices: A World Forum for Music Therapy, North America, 6,* Nov. 2006. Retrieved from https://normt.uib.no/index.php/voices/article/view/279

Wood, S. (2014). *The Performance of Community Music Therapy Evaluation.* (Unpublished doctoral dissertation). City University, London.

Wood, S., Verney, R., & Atkinson, J. (2004). From Therapy to Community: Making Music in Neurological Rehabilitation. In M. Pavlicevic & G. Ansdell (Eds.), *Community Music Therapy* (pp. 48–64). London: Jessica Kingsley Publishers.

Woodward, A. (2004). Music Therapy for Autistic Children and their Families: A Creative Spectrum. *British Journal of Music Therapy, 18*(1), 8–24.

Wosch, T., & Wigram, T. (Eds.). (2007). *Microanalysis in Music Therapy.* London: Jessica Kingsley Publishers.

Yinger, O. S., & Lapointe, L. L. (2012). Effects of Participation in a Group Music Therapy Voice Protocol (G-MTVP) on the Speech of Individuals with Parkinson's Disease. *Music Therapy Perspectives, 30*(1), 25–31.

York, E. (2006). Finding Voice: Feminist Music Therapy and Research with Women Survivors. In S. Hadley (Ed.), *Feminist Perspectives in Music Therapy* (pp. 245–265). Gilsum, NH: Barcelona Publishers.

Zare, M., Ebrahami, A., & Birashk, B. (2010). The Effects of Music Therapy on Reducing Agitation in Patients with Alzheimer's Disease, a Pre–Post Study. *International Journal of Geriatric Psychiatry, 25*(12), 1309–1310.

Index

A

Actor-network Theory, 124–26, 160
agendas, 23, 39, 89, 97, 117, 119, 122, 127, 139, 142
agreement, inter-rater, 139–40, 155, 180
Alzheimer's Disease, 38, 138, 174, 176, 179, 190
analysis, qualitative, 175
Ansdell, xii, xvi, 23, 27, 29, 31–32, 39, 42, 57, 134, 167–68, 180, 182, 186, 189
anxiety, 34, 37–38, 162, 171, 175, 180, 186–87
Assessment in Music Therapy, 77, 145, 147, 149, 171, 176, 181
autism, 38, 140, 189
Azoulay, 138, 168, 175, 186

B

Bellelli, 183
brain injury, 92, 129, 132, 168, 179
Bruscia, 5, 27, 36, 42, 136, 148, 170

C

care, 40, 70, 73, 98, 105, 115, 132, 175, 177
caregivers, 175, 184, 186
Caregiver Singing and Background Music in Dementia Care, 17, 52, 69, 79, 85, 144, 174, 181
care homes, xv, 9, 17, 35, 38, 65–66, 70–73, 75, 88, 97–105, 109, 111–14, 116–17, 121, 158
care plan, 78, 86, 104–5, 109, 114–15
change, xii–xiii, 15–16, 18, 24–26, 28, 37, 40, 56–57, 59, 72–74, 80, 102, 145–46, 148, 167–68
Character and Scope of Evaluation, 134
children's work, 37–38, 40, 48, 140, 169, 172, 174, 177, 179, 181, 188–89
choices, 4–6, 8–9, 16, 60, 62, 76, 86, 88–90, 96, 98–99, 121, 135, 145–46, 158
choir, 19, 65, 71–72

Client-therapist relationship in Coactive Musical Experience, 106, 180–81

collaborative work, 140–41, 182–83

communal, 22, 28–29, 60, 98, 145, 164

Communicative Musicality, xiii, 14, 180, 182–83, 187

community, 22–23, 28, 31–32, 41–42, 47–50, 52–53, 56–57, 90–91, 132–33, 135, 142, 144–45, 148–49, 182–83, 188–89

Community Music, 23, 29, 36, 141, 164, 182

Community Music Therapy, xi, 4, 29, 167–69, 172–73, 177, 180, 182–83, 185–86, 188–89

complexity, xiii–xiv, 7, 10, 12, 17, 21, 61–62, 77, 171

complexity theory, 59, 61

CoMT, xii–xvi, 3–12, 15–20, 26–36, 38–39, 42–44, 51–52, 85–89, 102–4, 109–11, 114–19, 121–22, 133–35, 138–41, 150–61

  character and scope of, xi, xiv, 39, 80, 127, 134

  context of, 30, 105, 110, 112, 115, 123–24, 127, 158

  discourse of, xii, 31

  value of, 113, 115–16, 133

CoMT evaluation, xv, 33, 103, 119, 122, 138–39, 141, 150, 148–54

CoMT literature, xiii, 16, 19, 44, 82, 96, 142

CoMT practice, xiv, xvi, 4, 80, 84, 109, 135, 142, 151

CoMT theory, 3, 5, 9, 26, 34, 42, 88

concepts, xv, 4, 6–7, 21–22, 25, 59–62, 69, 75, 81, 92–93, 96, 150, 155, 157–59, 161

conceptual tools, 74, 80, 82

contact, 10, 24, 75, 104, 121–22

Content, 71, 77–78, 86, 93, 98, 153

context, xiv–xv, 4–5, 7–9, 29–32, 61, 72, 84–88, 96–97, 99–100, 102–4, 109–12, 121, 123–27, 133–34, 153–55

Creative Music Therapy, 69, 181

creativity, xii, 14, 53–54, 91, 93, 148–49

Critiques of CoMT, 32, 43

culture, xiii, 14–15, 28, 84, 97, 113, 115, 160, 177, 181, 184

D

Defining Community Music Therapy, 3, 30, 184

Defining Music Therapy, 170

Deleuze, 14, 65, 160, 173

Deleuze and Guattari, 92–93, 95, 161, 174
dementia, 34–35, 38, 40–41, 97–98, 104, 109, 119–20, 123–24, 167, 169–71, 173–76, 178–79, 181, 183–84, 186–88

E

ecological approach, 5, 27–29, 41, 93
Effectiveness of Music Therapy, 139, 168, 171, 175, 179–80, 187
Effect of Baroque Music on Behavioural Disturbances, 181, 183
Effects of music therapy, 174, 176–77, 180, 185, 187–90
evaluation, 4, 8–9, 12, 33, 36, 38–39, 69, 73–75, 77–80, 83, 127, 129–58, 173, 176, 187
evaluation criteria, 19, 38, 43, 137, 155
evaluation form, 105–6, 114, 153
evaluation processes, 36, 74, 119, 123, 127, 134, 136–37, 139–40, 143, 145, 147
evaluation reports, 41, 135, 138, 154

F

FACETs of CoMT, xv, 3
facets of music therapy, 19, 44
families, 16, 28, 42, 56, 66, 75, 82, 97, 103, 109–11, 117, 122, 129, 131, 144
family members, 42–43, 49, 85, 108, 144, 151, 176
feminist music therapy, 39, 171, 189
formats, xiii–xiv, xvi, 8–9, 19, 23–24, 47–63, 65–66, 70, 72, 74–75, 84–90, 96–97, 133, 144–45, 155–58
functional interaction, 86–87, 143–46, 148, 158
Functional Interaction Matrix Assessment, 143, 149
functional skill, 87
functions, 20–21, 59, 86, 90, 94, 114, 143, 145–46

G

Goodchild, 93, 174
Götell, 35, 170, 174–75
group, 7–8, 23–24, 28, 41–42, 48, 52–56, 59–60, 62, 76, 79, 89–91, 144–46, 148–51, 157–58, 160

group music therapy, 38, 41, 48, 54–56, 66, 75, 79, 133, 170–71, 179–80, 187–89
Guattari, 65, 173

H

health, 5, 27–29, 43, 48, 88–89, 93, 100, 138–39, 168, 172, 175, 179, 181, 184, 186
health care, mental, 111, 116–18, 122–24, 184–85

I

improvisation, 12, 26, 49–51, 53–55, 67, 69–72, 97, 169–70, 184
IMTAP (Individualized Music Therapy Assessment Profile), 136, 169
inclusion, 29, 33, 88, 104, 141, 154, 169
Individual Music-Centered Assessment Profile, 136, 170
Individual Music Therapy Session, 24, 37, 48–50, 58, 60, 65, 69, 88, 147, 185, 188
interpersonal, 16, 28, 148, 185
interplay, 23, 88, 90, 146–47
interventions, clinical music therapy, 34, 62–63, 135, 140–42, 167, 174, 182, 186
interviews, 74–75, 105, 111–12, 115–17

J

Jacobsen, 40, 176–77
JUNK, 5, 96, 99, 102–3, 117

K

Kenny, 28, 32, 177, 183
Kittay, 36, 178

L

Latour, xvi, 124–26, 160–61, 178

M

matrix, xiii–xv, 9–11, 13–15, 21–22, 25–26, 44–45, 58, 60, 66, 68, 87, 89, 92, 95, 157–58

matrix model, 19–20, 57, 66, 92, 123

Matrix of Aims, 66–96

Matrix of Content, 98–128

Matrix of Context, 97, 123

Matrix of discourses, 9, 123, 158

Matrix of Evaluation, 57, 129–56

Matrix of Formats, 47–63

Matrix of music, 10–11, 45

matrix thinking, 7, 9, 12, 22, 24, 62, 89, 158

Method of Music Therapy Assessment, 189

microanalysis, 105, 112–14, 137, 189

musical communication, 85, 106, 150

musical experience, 16, 18, 42–43, 45, 59–60, 62, 69, 92, 104, 106, 109–12, 130–31, 133, 151, 153–54

musical formats, 19, 34, 57–58, 92

musical interests, 49

musicality, xv, 14, 21, 67, 88, 127, 131, 136, 144–48, 151, 159, 187

musical operations, 21, 58, 92

Music-centered Music Therapy, xiv, 20, 52, 154, 167

music-making, xiii, 8, 19, 23, 25, 30, 57, 59, 61, 72, 82, 98, 102, 115, 172–73

Music Matrix, 13–26

Music psychotherapy and CoMT, 168, 186–87

music therapy
  culture-centred, 20, 186
  ecological, 20
  effects of, 37–38, 40, 179
  improvisational, 38, 52, 57
  resource-oriented, xiv, 6, 20

music therapy assessment, 137, 139–41, 148, 169, 172, 176, 178–79, 181, 184, 189

music therapy discourse, 9, 60, 106, 108, 158

music therapy evaluation, 10, 35, 37–38, 41–42, 114, 136–43, 150, 153–55, 183

music therapy literature, xiv, xvi, 23, 41, 60, 134, 155

music therapy practice, xii, 24, 31, 35, 47, 72, 74–75, 82, 88, 95, 115, 134–35, 140, 142–43, 162
music therapy theory, 29, 32, 70, 133, 186

N

network, 31, 59–61, 103, 109–10, 112–13, 115, 119, 121–22, 124–25, 151, 159
Nordoff Robbins, 20, 48–49, 60, 69, 73, 102–3, 106, 122, 137, 139, 180–81
Nursing Home Residents, 98, 174, 180, 182, 186, 188

O

observation, xv, 3, 14, 69, 79, 130, 142

P

paramusical processes, 61, 154
participants, 23, 30, 36, 42–43, 47–49, 52, 54, 57, 102, 105, 134–35, 138, 141, 144, 151–52
Pavlicevic, xvi, 14, 19, 29–31, 42, 60, 134, 137, 157, 180, 182–83, 186–87, 189
Pavlicevic & Ansdell, xiii, 19–20, 22, 27, 30–31
performance, 7–8, 31, 33–34, 54–55, 71–72, 82, 87, 94, 117–19, 125, 130, 143, 145, 152–53, 167–68
Performance in Music Therapy, 30, 33, 43, 101–2, 125, 151, 177, 189
performativity, 7, 9–10, 12, 43, 88, 124–25, 129, 142, 150, 153, 156–59, 161
persona, 11, 19, 51, 56
person-centred care, values of, 98
personhood, 7, 28, 41, 93, 114, 148, 150–51, 157, 159
piano, 26, 56, 67–68, 99–100, 121, 147
planning, 47–48, 53, 61, 74–77, 79–81, 86
playing, 8, 16, 22, 25–26, 49, 51–52, 54–56, 61, 67–68, 81, 101, 126, 132, 144, 165
poetry, 13–14, 65, 69–70, 99, 160
Psychotherapy, 168, 170, 172, 184, 188

R

Recognizing CoMT, 28–37, 39–45
recovery, 10–11, 48, 129–31, 184
Reflexivity, xii, 74, 85–86, 138
research, 37–39, 41, 98, 118–21, 123–24, 139, 142, 164, 170, 174, 189
researcher, xv, 120, 123–24, 126, 176
rhizome, xv, 4, 65, 94–95, 155
Robbins, 20, 48, 60, 137, 139, 181
Rolvsjord, 6, 20, 23, 39, 134, 184–85
Ruud, 20, 28, 30, 36, 137, 155, 181, 184

S

scrap, xiv, 47, 53–54, 56, 100–101
scrap heap, 52–53, 100
Scrap Metal Project, 47, 49, 65, 100, 133
singing, 16, 22, 52, 66, 68, 70–71, 77, 99, 104, 109, 114, 170, 174–76, 184, 187
skills, 8, 11, 24, 48–49, 80, 87–89, 91, 99, 108, 147, 149
society, 20, 23, 28–29, 39, 93
songs, 11, 69–71, 92, 100
sounds, 3–4, 11–13, 15, 19, 26, 51, 54, 78, 100, 104, 120, 126–27, 147, 152
Stige, xvi, 17, 20, 22, 27–28, 30, 38–39, 42, 44, 134, 137–39, 150–52, 177–78, 183, 186–87
Stige & Aarø, xiv, 6, 27–28, 152
story, 49–50, 52, 56, 62, 96, 101, 112, 118, 127, 129, 177
Suzuki, 40, 186
SW, 76, 78, 80–81, 83, 113, 115
system, 5–7, 20, 24–26, 28, 59–62, 79, 84, 86, 89, 94–95, 118, 122, 138, 152, 155

T

theory, xii, xiv–xvi, 4, 8–12, 16, 19, 29–32, 39, 44, 65, 156–57, 159, 170, 177, 184

V

Vaillancourt, 39, 134, 138, 153, 172, 188
values, xv–xvi, 4, 7, 9–10, 30, 50, 73, 108–11, 115, 117, 121–22, 133–34, 152, 154–55, 158
Verney, 47, 189

W

Wigram, 40, 137, 141, 168, 174, 177, 189
Wood, xiii, 24, 47, 57–58, 73, 189
workforce, 115–18, 122
workplace, 18, 28, 57, 69, 79, 84–85, 143, 155
workshops, 8, 24, 48, 52, 54, 57, 90, 140, 146, 157

[Created with **TExtract** / www.Texyz.com]